The Complete

CLARICE CLIFF

A Collectors Handbook

Contributors

Howard and Pat Watson

Jonathan Daltrey

Edited by

F J Salmon

Francis Joseph
London
ISBN 1870703-78-2

Acknowledgements

The staff of Stoke-on-Trent City Library are thanked for providing access to the Clarice Cliff memorabilia in the Wilkinson Collection.

The staff of Stoke-on-Trent City Museum and Art Gallery are thanked for help with research and for essential background information.

Invaluable help in the identification and dating of patterns has been provided by Leonard R. Griffin and Louis Meisel's book *Clarice Cliff and the Bizarre Affair* and by the quarterly reviews and other publications of the Clarice Cliff Collectors Club.

Jonathan Daltrey and Alan Brooks of BananaDance Limited.

Christie's South Kensington are also warmly thanked for supplying photographs.

Finally, all friends, dealers and customers are thanked for the interesting discussions and comments they have made to us during the preparation of this book.

© Francis Joseph Publications 2003

Published in the UK
Francis Joseph Publications
5 Southbrook Mews, London SE12 8LG

Typeset in Great Britain by
E J Folkard Print Services, 199 Station Road, Crayford, Kent DA1 3QF

Printed in England

ISBN 1870703 78 2

Contents

How to use this book

To avoid the need for lengthy descriptions and to make reference quick and simple, every effort has been made to illustrate as many as possible of Clarice Cliff's major patterns by colour photographs.

Patterns were phased out after a long or short period according to popularity, and where possible the date of discontinuation has been given, but it should be noted that with tableware in particular, matchings could be ordered which would be specially decorated to the customer's requirements. In order to replace broken items, the paintress would refer to the pattern-book for designs which had become obsolete. This means that replacement items may not only be considerably later in date than the original but that also they may carry a different backstamp.

Bold words indicate a known pattern name.

Italic words indicate shapes.

If there is an unofficial popular name for a pattern this is left in normal type.

When referring to the price guide, it is important that the contents of this book be read first. The work of Clarice Cliff was not produced in a steady numbered and catalogued way, and therefore, to overcome complications, it has been necessary to put her designs into three broad ranges of popularity. From this it is possible to apply the pattern of an item into one of the three ranges and come up with a price that is a broad reflection of the auction value.

When buying or selling Clarice Cliff, the collector

The Appliqué range, with its all-over colouring technique and its fairy-tale subject-matter – castles, caravans, wind and water mills, mountains and exotic birds – has always been popular with collectors. Here, a single-handled Lotus jug in Appliqué Avignon. £5000-£8000/$7400-$12,240. (Collection of Annie and Ian Tickler)

Delecia Anemone (£600/$890).

must bear in mind that the dealer or auction house will have a mark-up on the price they are prepared to pay you. Therefore, the price you receive for a piece of Clarice Cliff, may be 20-40 per cent lower than the prices given in this book.

The main aim of any guide, though, is to give a cross-section of the market at a given time. Prices will change from day to day, but for the casual buyer, it is important to at least distinguish the pieces that are worth £5 or £50 from those that are worth £500 or £5000 and we believe that this reference guide has achieved that aim.

Appliqué Lugano. £6000-£8000/$8880-$12,240.

Introduction

For those of us who can remember a Thirties childhood, it is easy to see why Clarice Cliff's Bizarre Ware came as a breath of fresh air in the days of the Depression, when the colour of Horlicks was the prevailing colour of the middle-class home. Even if we cannot remember seeing a single piece of it ourselves, we can imagine the impact it must have had. Throughout the war, the British people suffered severely from colour starvation. No wonder that in later life we turned to Clarice Cliff as eagerly as that earlier generation when she first launched her designs and took the pottery establishment by storm.

The rediscovery of Clarice Cliff is a story in itself, and modern collectors will be forever indebted to Martin Battersby, John Jesse, Harvey Daniels, Clive Collins, Davy How and a few other early enthusiasts who, along with Clarice Cliff herself,

Appliqué Idyll. £500-£700/$740-$1070.

lent items for the historic 1972 exhibition at the Brighton Museum and Art Gallery which set the ball rolling. The publication by Noel Tovey's Fulham Road Art Gallery, L'Odeon of *Clarice Cliff*, written by Peter Wentworth-Sheilds and Kay Johnson, in 1976 was another landmark, and so was the formation by Len Griffin in 1982 of the Clarice Cliff Collectors Club.

My own collection was begun early in 1982 when on holiday in Harrogate. I bought a small *Tulips* vase for £4. Attracted by her brilliant use of shape and colour, I collected more pieces and gathered more background knowledge, coming to realise the extent of Clarice Cliff's influence on pottery design and the skill with which she drew on an enormously wide range of sources for her inspiration, from the flowers and scenery around her Potteries home to the classic Art Deco styles of the day.

Some pieces turned up in unusual places – a **Gibraltar** *Bonjour* jug holding back curtains on a windowsill, a **Red Tulip** plaque almost thrown away because it no longer fitted in with a new colour scheme, a **Red Roofs** vase offered over the phone by the original owner from the Thirties. Not long afterwards, Channel 4's *Pottery Ladies* series aroused considerable public interest, and Clarice Cliff's name was beginning to become a household word again, as it had been during her lifetime.

Soon it became clear that an illustrated guide to her work would be welcome, as a handy pocket reference book for collectors to use to identify her patterns and shapes, and to provide a pictorial introduction to the work of Clarice Cliff in general, and in 1988 *Collecting Clarice Cliff* was published, followed by *The Wonderful World of Clarice Cliff* and *The Clarice Cliff Price Guide*. With these three books now out of print, the

Aurea in the foreground on a Coronet jug (£400/$590). On the left, 'Floreat' and Sungay (£400/$590 each), centre Pastel Melon (£700/$1035) with Orange Latona Dahlia (£1000/$1480), on the right Lydiat on an oval Bonjour jug (£300/$445) with an Athens jug in Blue Chintz (£700/$1035) to the rear. (Courtesy of Christie's)

A Conical coffee set in 'Moonflower' (£2500/$3700). (Courtesy of Christie's)

present book offers the information they contained, updated and with many new photographs, plus an up-to-date price guide, together with a selection of backstamps to aid dating and identification.

The aim once again has been to be concise and practical, but at the same time as always to illustrate the astonishing range and variety of the work of the woman who will always be, for me, the greatest of all our Pottery Ladies, to salute her recent centenary.

Howard Watson.

A Bonjour shape coffee set in Cabbage Flower (£2500/$3700). (Courtesy of Christie's)

A Hundred Years of Clarice Cliff

Early Days

Clarice Cliff was born in January, 1899, though it's sometimes said she was in the habit of knocking a year off her age in order to bring herself firmly forward into the twentieth century. Not that she need have worried – no one could ever have called her an old-fashioned girl. With strongly-marked features, deep blue eyes and sleek black hair drawn smoothly back into a stylish bun, she made up in personality what she lacked in inches. Full of determination and never afraid of hard work, she made herself the fashionable clothes she couldn't afford to buy, and decorated her bedroom in orange, yellow, gold and black, a bizarre combination that was a sign of things to come. For Clarice Cliff had been born into the Potteries, and once she got her hands on it, the British pottery industry would never be the same again.

The situation hardly looked promising at first. One of eight children, with five sisters and two brothers, she grew up in the average working-class family of the day, respectable, God-fearing people who paid their way but had little left over for the luxuries of life, and who never in their wildest dreams would have expected a child of theirs to cause a stir of any sort. Harry Thomas Cliff, Clarice's father, worked as an iron-moulder at Fullers' factory and he and his wife Ann (née Machin) lived with their family, large but in those days by no means exceptionally so, at 19 Meir Street, Tunstall, moving when more room was needed to a house in Edwards Street nearby. Tunstall is one of the six North Staffordshire towns making up the district of Stoke-on-Trent -

Ravel, another early pattern of branches and leaves, usually green and orange £75-£700/$110-$1070.

Occasionally it came in blue and orange (£250/$370), while in blue and maroon it was Brunella (£250-£300/$370-$460).

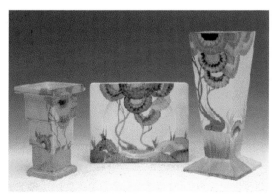

The "etching" technique blended brushstrokes together. A Biarritz plate in Aurea (£350/$520), with a tall vase in Rhodanthe (£700/$1035) and another vase in Viscaria (£700/$1035) .

the others are Burslem, Hanley, Stoke, Fenton and Longton - which have a long and happily on-going history of pottery production which may well date back to Neolithic times. Clarice and her brothers and sisters made their way to school past potteries large and small, each with its own bottle ovens belching out smoke so that thick black clouds hung overhead obscuring the sunshine. Though neither of their parents worked in the pottery industry, they did have an aunt who was the "missus" of Meakin's decorating shop in Tunstall, so they had some idea of what went on in the factories, or pot-banks as they were called by local people. No doubt they chuckled between themselves over the quaint names given to the various occupations - mouldrunners, casters, dippers, fettlers and, of course, the saggarmakers' bottom-knockers. But whether any of them saw themselves going into a pot-bank in the future, who can say? The end product was fine and dainty, but the process that brought it into being was hot, grimy and backbreaking. Unless, of course, you rose to the top . . . .

Green café-au-lait sponging applied on top of Viscaria, with moulded items in Marguerite. Plate (£200/$295), Cup and Saucer (£100/$150), Honey/Jam Pot (£150/$220).

Clarice began her education at the High Street Elementary School, while the other children attended another local school. This was so that she could deliver a packed lunch to a family friend en route, a delaying factor that often got her into trouble for lateness when she finally arrived. An average pupil, she did show some early skill in art, and was, as she later said, "entrusted to make large papier-mâché maps, built up on nails of varying heights, coloured for use in geography lessons". At ten she went on to the Summerbank Road School where, probably with local industry in mind, clay modelling was included in the art curriculum. After school she began to call in on her way home to see her aunt at work, and out of this perhaps came her eventual choice of career.

The school-leaving age in those days was thirteen,

In the foreground, a vase in 'Branch and Squares' (£900-£1200/$1330-$1835) with a Broth vase behind (£900-£1200/$1330-$1835). (Courtesy of Christie's)

9

and when in 1912 Clarice finally left school she embarked on a seven-year apprenticeship with the firm of Lingard, Webster and Company at the Swan Factory near her home, to train as a freehand painter. For a five and a half day week she earned one shilling (five pence, ludicrous now, but an acceptable sum with fair purchasing power in those days), out of which she had to buy brushes and palette knives as well as handing over most of the money to her mother for her board and lodgings, like the rest of the family.

Clarice's training in those early years was to stand her in good stead later on, when she would need practical knowledge to enable her to produce designs suitable to fit on every item of tableware, large or small. She learnt to handle a paintbrush - or "pencil" as it was called in the trade - so that she could apply the colour accurately without guidelines and with confident, bold strokes. It was painstaking work that gave her a realistic sense of the possibilities and limitations of the method when, years later, she was to oversee the growing talents of the paintresses in the Bizarre Workshop. Memories of these early days made her patient with her young team and she was remembered as never asking them to do anything that was beyond her own skills.

After three years at Lingard, Webster and Company, Clarice decided in 1915 to move on to another Tunstall firm, Hollinshead and Kirkham Limited, of the Unicorn Works, today often referred to by collectors as "H. and K." The factory produced attractive tableware and fancies, many of them decorated by the process known as lithography, a form of transfer printing, and it was this that Clarice was keen to learn. The technique was quite different from the handpainting method she was now so familiar with, and once again she was unconsciously building up skills she would make use of in the years ahead. In the early

Clouvre Bluebell, a plaque from the Clouvre range of 1930-31 (£2500/$3700). (Courtesy of Christie's)

A Blue Chintz jug (£700/$1035) with a grapefruit dish (£250/$370) in Orange Chintz and a coffee cup (£600/$890) with solid handle in Green Chintz.

A single-handled Lotus jug in Melon (£3000/$4440).

Thirties, for patterns like "Sunshine" and "Flora", she employed the "print and enamel" method, a combination of both lithography in the form of a transfer outline and handpainting to add the colour. This form of decoration was used very successfully by firms like Shelley and Susie Cooper Productions, both throughout the 1930s and postwar, though Clarice's print and enamel patterns were never as popular, either in her own day or with collectors now, as her wholly handpainted patterns.

Perhaps her move to Hollinshead and Kirkham created some friction in the family, as due to concern that she keep up her handpainting and modelling interests, it was decided that, despite the expense, Clarice should attend evening classes at the Tunstall School of Art. It must have been a busy life for the sixteen-year-old with a long factory day followed by further tuition in the evening. Luckily she was able to win a scholarship to help with the fees, but the curriculum at the art school was known to be somewhat unimaginative in those days, and later Clarice commented wryly, ''drawing from plaster casts and vases of honesty were the sum total of tuition''.

Moving on

Before long, though, she was on the move again. By 1916 the absence of the young men drafted into the forces to fight in the trenches of the First World War had left tempting vacancies in potteries elsewhere and with her newly-acquired talent for lithography she was able to secure an apprenticeship at A. J. Wilkinson's Royal Staffordshire Pottery in Burslem. This was to be a crucial step with far-reaching effects not only for Clarice but for the entire pottery industry. When she first went there, she probably knew nothing of the strenuous efforts already made by Arthur Colley Austin Shorter, Wilkinson's managing director, to expand the business into Canadian and

Vases in Gayday (£350/$520), Summer Dawn (£250/$370), 'Double V' (£600/$890) and Blue Daisy (£900/$1330). (Courtesy of Christie's)

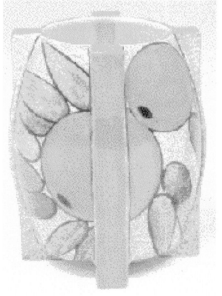

Oranges with café-au-lait (£700-£900/$1035-$1375).

South American markets to counteract the slump caused by the American import tariff. By the time of the next crisis, the Depression of the Thirties, it would be Clarice herself whose talent and hard work kept the firm afloat. For the moment, though, she was still learning her trade. A tram ride and a brisk walk took her to the canalside factory, adding an extra half-hour in travelling time at each end of her working day. Once there, employed originally as an apprentice lithographer, she moved on to learn "modelling in clay, keeping pattern and shape books up to date, very fine filigree gilding with a pen, tracing spiders' webs, butterflies etc, to hide small imperfections on expensive ware . . . During this time I gained very useful knowledge of the making and firing of pottery". At the same time she was continuing to study at evening classes, moving eventually to the Burslem School of Art, where the standard of tuition, under teachers like Gordon Forsyth, was more interesting and varied. With time spent in dressmaking, decorating her bedroom, teaching in Sunday School and church attendance, her days were full.

The intelligent interest she was showing in every aspect of the pottery process was noted with approval by the decorating manager at the factory, Jack Walker. Realising she had more than average ability, he suggested to Colley Shorter, his brother-in-law, that she should be promoted to work in the studio used by John Butler and Fred Ridgeway, the firm's top designers. It was on their fine quality lustre ranges like Oriflamme, Rubaiyat and Tibetan that Clarice Cliff was entrusted with the task of disguising flaws in the glaze with gilded decorations. In 1923 a note referring to a plaque by Fred Ridgeway in the firm's archives states, "CC does the gold". The following year she was being allowed to model small figurines including men in Arab dress and a native boy, all marked "Clarice C.24" and an old market woman marked

Oranges with café-au-lait (£750/$1110).

A small teapot in Bamboo (£300/$445) with teaware in Honeydew (£200/$295), a Cabbage Flower coffee cup (£200/$295) and a teapot in Lydiat (£300/$445).

Candleholders in Gayday (£250/$370) and 'Sunray Leaves' (£350/$520) with smaller ones in Lily Orange (£150/$220) and Autumn (£250/$370).

12

"CC24". Her promotion had brought her not only increased prestige and higher wages, but greater freedom to follow her interests. A few years earlier, in 1920, the success of Colley Shorter – or "Mr. Colley" as he was always known at the firm - in expanding their markets had led to the firm buying the Newport Pottery adjoining their premises, and here in 1925 Clarice was given space to pursue her talent for photography with a view to producing photographs for use in the factory's publicity. She had gradually become a prominent member of the administrative team and as such was now spending considerable time with Mr. Colley himself. This inevitably caused comment, he being a married man seventeen years her senior, with two daughters and an invalid wife. Though they were, and continued to be, extremely careful to avoid scandal, their close association was to become even closer as Clarice pursued her single-minded determination to achieve recognition of her talents as a designer.

It is difficult today to realise the enormity of the step Clarice took in leaving home at this point. Generally girls remained with their families till they married, patiently accumulating bed linen, tableware and household utensils in their "bottom drawer" ready for their wedding day. Consternation must have been caused in the Cliff household when Clarice announced her intention of moving to a one-bedroom flat over a beauty salon at 40, Snow Hill, Hanley. Whether her decision had anything to do with her increasing intimacy with Colley Shorter or not, no doubt tongues wagged and gossip was rife. Luckily, with jobs at stake, no one was foolish enough to comment openly. Provided the proprieties were observed, Clarice's good name was safe. But perhaps it was to ensure this that in 1927 she discreetly vanished from the scene. Between 14 March and 26 May, she took a short course in

Lily Orange on a triangular vase (£700/$1035), Lily Brown (£300/$445) on a small vase and Sunrise (£1000/$1480).

'Blue-eyed Marigold' on a small pot (£300/$445), 'Garland' on a bowl (£300/$445) and Kelverne on a Bonjour jampot (£300/$445).

The brown colourway of Kelverne in the Trieste shape (£500/$740).

sculpture at the Royal College of Art in London, paid for by her employers. She made such rapid progress that at the end of the course her tutor wrote to Colley, "There is little doubt she has native ability . . . . the figure she has just modelled shows a surprising advance on her work two months ago, and if financial circumstances had not to be taken into account, but only the development of her talent to be considered, I should say, go on studying for two or three years". What, we might wonder, would have happened if she could have followed that advice? But Clarice Cliff was a working girl, not a wealthy student, and after a brief holiday in Paris, again paid for by the factory as she was researching Continental design trends, she returned to Newport Pottery to pursue her career.

Forest Leaves breakfast set (£250/$370). (Collection of Des Jones)

A Defining Moment

At Newport Pottery a studio awaited her and it was here that Bizarre was born. Left untouched since the Wilkinsons takeover in 1920, undecorated whiteware had gathered dust on its shelves and this was handed over to Clarice to see what she could make of it. "This huge stock," she wrote years later, "had always interested me, and presented a challenge!" Undismayed by the dust and the dated, old-fashioned shapes, she plunged ahead and transformed the pottery with a riot of vivid colours. Realising her team of young apprentice paintresses needed practice first on simple, geometric patterns, she devised for them colourful combinations of shapes and colours which quickly converted the dreary whiteware into startling, modern pottery unlike any seen before in the currently rather staid industry. "As these were the days of short-time and unemployment," she was to write many years later, "it was very easy to get girls straight from school . . . a few of them with an aptitude for drawing were put straight to work . . . Between guidelines they drew simple diamonds

Passion Fruit (£100/$150).

An octagonal bowl in Sliced Fruit (£300/$445).

14

which were then filled in with bright colours by other girls". This, nowadays usually called Original Bizarre, sometimes betrays its humble origin by embossed twigs and berries ignored by the early paintresses as they piled on the paint, but still clearly visible like Victorian ghosts below the surface of the pattern. "Meanwhile a sizeable amount of goods were accumulating. These were a cause of much merriment and derision to the travellers," Clarice remembered.

Despite the jeers, after a preview at the British Industries Fair of 1928, where it was launched as "Bizarre by Clarice Cliff", those who had made merry and derided it were forced to eat their words when, with sixty dozen items ready, the range justified Clarice's faith in it and orders began to pour in. The first stocks were swiftly sold out and the team of paintresses hurriedly expanded to set to work to replace them. Regarded at first as an attractive novelty, it was clear now that Bizarre was here to stay, and with her name on every piece that was sold, Clarice Cliff was established as a ceramic designer on a par with those other household names of the day, Susie Cooper, Charlotte Rhead and Mollie Hancock. Professional success for Clarice, however, carried with it considerably more weight than for those other, highly respected women designers. For her it meant that she need no longer fear the raised eyebrows or the covert sneer. Her success was keeping them all safe from the dole queue, and they better not forgot it! Equally, the management, including Colley Shorter, were well aware of their obligation to her. If she was to be "poached" by another factory, the consequences would have been dire. She had proved a highly successful investment and they would reap the rewards for years to come. Little wonder, then, that they were careful not to offend her, though that is not to say they approved of the situation. Fred Ridgeway, for some reason, had

Three items from the My Garden range and an incised Scraphito bowl (£50-£100/$75-$155) .

A Conical sugar shaker (£750/$1110) and an Athens jug in Nasturtium (£600/$890).

Items from the Nuage range. Two vases (£500/$740 each), Plate (£200/$295), Preserve Jar (£400/$590)

15

never liked Clarice, while recently, perhaps understandably in the circumstances, Jack Walker had also begun to treat her with reserve. Since by now she had lost the old camaraderie of the shop floor, she flung herself into her work, moving on from the early geometric designs to her first - and most long-lasting - floral pattern, "Crocus". As the orders rolled in, her team was increased by the addition of more girls, as well as several boys. They worked in a former store-room in a warehouse alongside the canal, while she spent most of her time in her studio. The Bizarre shop was supervised by an efficient and kindly "missus" Lily Slater. Backed up by clever advertising and frequent in-store demonstrations, the demand for Bizarre continued to grow, and in 1930 Clarice was appointed Company Art Director, her youth and bubbly personality a considerable asset for publicity purposes. Newspaper and magazine articles described her meteoric rise to fame in glowing terms, and with her ruby-red Austin Seven named Jenny, bought for £60, her high wages and her stylish clothes - no need for home dressmaking now! – she was all set for a spectacular career. Called "the Sunshine Girl", creator of "Happy China", her name became synonymous with everything modern and up-beat, a far cry from her early days.

So popular was "Crocus" in all its many variations (Original Crocus, the pastel Spring Crocus, Blue Crocus, the yellow and orange Sungleam Crocus, Peter Pan Crocus with black silhouettes of trees, and the very rare Purple Crocus) that "Lupin" the pattern next in the pattern book, seems never to have been put into full production. "Crocus" continued to be in demand throughout the Thirties on both conventional shapes and on the striking shapes Clarice designed herself. More floral patterns followed – "Gayday", based on asters but using the same palette as "Crocus",

Marigold on a Mallet shaped vase £5000-£7000/$7400-$10,710.

Red Tulip on an Isis vase (£2500/$3700).

"Sungay" the sunny blue and yellow version of "Gayday", "Lily" in both orange and brown colourways, "Gardenia" and "Cowslip" in several variations and many more exotic renderings of familiar flowers. Stylised landscapes came next, many of them featuring quaint country cottages set among Disney-esque trees and bushes. With outlets in all the main department stores and china chains, a need soon arose for a second range to accompany Bizarre, and this Clarice gave the name Fantasque.

Moselle (£700/$1035).

''Bizarre was usually sold to one customer in a town, So Fantasque was supposed to be a little different and sold to another shop," she blithely explained later. A subterfuge perhaps on a par with the crafty tax-spreading device of issuing some of the pottery with a Wilkinson's stamp instead of sending it all out under the Newport imprint!

Waterlily, used on a large range of items (£50/$75).

By now Clarice was involved in all three aspects of ceramic design - pattern, shape and surface texture. From the beginning she had experimented with glaze variations such as Latona and the very tricky Inspiration, closely followed by Scraphito, Appliqué and Delecia, all, along with Café au Lait, Nuage and Damask Rose, in varying degrees successful, with only Patina for some reason less so. As the years passed and design trends moved into softer mode, she also used what was known as the "etching" technique, for "Rhodanthe" and its variations and the gentle landscape "Trallee", with the brushstrokes blended to avoid hard edges. Her "My Garden" and "Celtic Harvest" ranges were both gently moulded, and she even experimented with a different type of clay for the "Goldstone" range. Some plain, classic shapes were issued with a smooth, celadon-type glaze but were, perhaps, too different from her earlier lively styles to prove popular under her name. Restraint was not something the public expected from Clarice Cliff!

'Crest', a very rare pattern on a strong Art Deco shape Stamford teapot and creamer (£2000/$2960).

With so much work already on her hands, Clarice became even busier in 1932, when she was asked to take part in a time-consuming and not ultimately successful experiment to involve leading contemporary artists with the ailing pottery industry by asking them to create patterns for use on tableware. The artists concerned included Dame Laura Knight, who seems to have been the most enthusiastic and successful, designing both highly original patterns and shapes, Eva Crofts, best known as a textile designer, Duncan Grant and Vanessa Bell, formerly of Roger Fry's Omega Workshop, and Gordon Forsyth who had by now moved on from the Burslem School of Art to take charge of art education for the whole area. Public response to the results of this enterprise was muted, though the tableware was exhibited both here and abroad, but auction houses today usually catalogue it as "Commissioned Work" in Clarice Cliff sales, and certain pieces do now frequently fetch high prices. Left to herself, though, it seems unlikely Clarice would have ever have commissioned these items. She had quite enough to do as it was, and the whole thing must have been a frustrating waste of time for her.

No doubt when it was all over she turned with relief to her normal day-to-day routine, to find that popular tastes had altered and the demand for her earlier exuberant patterns had declined. By the mid-Thirties people had less money in their pockets and tended to be sternly practical when it came to spending what they did have. Tableware was now in demand, fancies less so, with the majority of ordinary customers. Celebrities, however, continued to visit the factory and the London trade fairs for photo-opportunities with the famous Clarice Cliff and stars of stage, screen and radio appeared in the press with their purchases. Embroidery transfers and crochet patterns to complement her designs were included

Newport (£100-£400/$150-$610 per item).

Cups and saucers in Cherry (£200/$295), Gardenia (£500/$740) and Pastel Autumn (£300/$445).

Tableware in the Odilon shape, in Lodore (£100-£200/$150-$305 per item).

18

in the popular women's magazines of the day, and "Woman's Journal" even commissioned sets of dinner and tea-ware exclusive to its readers. Clarice was still a force to be reckoned with, but the times were a-changing.

The range name Fantasque was phased out in 1934 and the even more famous Bizarre in 1937, and this seems to have marked the end of an era. Clarice would go on designing – she could lay claim to over two thousand patterns in all, as well as at least five hundred new shapes, plus novelties and facemasks – but now she aimed at a lighter, more discreet touch. A few last bold landscapes, for example, "Forest Glen" with its vivid Delecia runnings, and its other colourway, "Newlyn", and the seaside scene, "Clovelly", rang down the curtain, and then she turned to the more restrained "Capri", "Napoli" and "Taormina" to accompany her pretty "My Garden" bowls and vases into the shops. The "Waterlily" range, also delicate and, perhaps more importantly, economical to produce, boosted sales. With a judicious mixture of market research and the trimming of production costs, Clarice kept the show on the road. Only the outbreak of the Second World War in September 1939, put a stop to her efforts. It was now all change, in every department of her life.

It had been good while it lasted, not only for Clarice but for her team. Dismal though the factory conditions were in those days, the Bizarre Girls had been allowed a radio and encouraged to sing at their benches, an unusual concession which in fact cut down on gossiping and sent production up by twenty-five per cent. Trips to local beauty spots and carnival parades in aid of charity encouraged the team spirit, and many of the girls enjoyed breaks from routine when they took part in in-store demonstrations in London and elsewhere. They were considered the elite of the pot-banks and with status went job security. In

Two items of Christine in Bonjour, with a Sunshine Stamford teapot (£600/$890) and a Tartan jampot (£250/$370).

A small Cherry Blossom vase (£100/$150), a May Blossom sugar shaker (£250/$370) and a Biarritz plate (£75/$110).

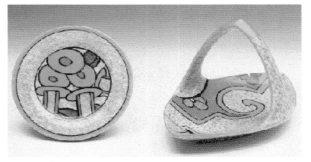

A 'Bobbins' biscuit plate (£250/$370) and a sweet-dish in Lisbon (£400/$590).

return they were expected to accept the demands of good timekeeping and strict quality control. That it was a happy time in their lives is clear from their comments long afterwards, speaking of generous wedding-presents and outings to the seaside.

Wartime and After

Now, with the death of Colley Shorter's wife a few weeks after the outbreak of war, Clarice and Colley were married just over a year later, though they did not announce it until the following November. With Newport Pottery requisitioned by the government, work was transferred to the main factory, but before long the decoration of pottery was banned for the duration. Only a small amount of banded ware was allowed to be made, for the Australian and New Zealand markets. Now living at Colley's large Art Nouveau mansion, "Chetwynd", set in beautiful grounds, Clarice must have had mixed feelings about the situation. Personal happiness had come at a time when events beyond her control had put an end to her artistic career. She helped where she could at Wilkinson's, arranging for "utility ware", as it was called, to be sent out to customers, but the plain white pieces must have seemed heartbreakingly ugly when she remembered the brighter days of Bizarre.

This complete break with her creative life perhaps explains why those days were never to return. When peace finally came in 1945, Clarice was forced to realise, as she said, "The mid-century look is towards the traditional, so we find modernised reproductions of the traditional in pottery the most popular." Colley and Clarice took to travelling abroad to find new outlets and to research possible lines that would sell. These included transfer patterns of country scenes, floral prints and, when the time came, the Coronation Ware of 1953. At the factory, Clarice's role had

A Conical tea for two set in Black Umbrellas (£5000/$7400). (Courtesy of Christie's)

Two Delecia Daisy plates (£250/$370 each) with a 'Geometric Flowers' (£500/$740) tazza, a 'Stroud' octagonal plate (£100/$150) and a large Red Trees and House tazza (£500/$740). (Courtesy of Christie's)

become mainly administrative. The world she had known was gone forever, and change, as it usually is, was in some ways for the better and in others for the worse. Wages had improved, and that could only be good for the workers on the factory floor, but it meant handpainting was now too expensive a method for the profit-conscious management, and transfers had once again come into their own. Changes in pre-war production methods, through the introduction of first, gas-fired ovens and then electricity, had banished the pall of smoke that used to hang over the Potteries, a welcome change for health and the environment, but as technology advanced vast machines replaced many workers, powder being poured in at one end and cups and saucers by the thousand coming out at the other, needing only a quick transfer decoration to send them on their way by the container-load to markets in South America.

It is perhaps no wonder that when, sadly, Colley Shorter died in December, 1963, aged 81, Clarice, left alone, no longer wished to keep on the factories. Her world had changed beyond recognition now, and she was ready to retire to her peaceful home and her beloved garden. A providential offer from Midwinter in 1964 led to the sale of the factories by the middle of the following year, and by the end of the decade Midwinter itself had been absorbed into the rapidly expanding Wedgwood Group. Meanwhile, at "Chetwynd", Clarice Cliff Shorter, as she was now known, spent much of her time cataloguing Colley Shorter's vast collection of art and antiques, from which she presented a selection in his memory to the Newcastle under Lyme Museum. An "Archers" fan, she listened to the radio but was hostile to television, which was now becoming so popular. She kept in touch with some of the Bizarre girls, and when she heard that Clarice Cliff pottery was beginning to be collected, she

Plates (left hand side) 'Feather and Leaves' (£300/$445), 'Fruitburst' (£400/$590) and 'Zap' (café-au-lait) (£500/$740), (right hand side) 'New Flag' (£500/$740), Latona Tree (£500/$740) on a pink ground and 'Sunrise' (£600/$890). (Courtesy of Christie's)

A Conical jug in 'Circle Tree' (£1200/$1775) and a twin-handled Lotus jug in 'Lightning' (£4000-£5000/$5920-$7650). (Courtesy of Christie's)

expressed amusement and shunned any publicity. As far as she was concerned, those days were over.

However, early in 1972, Brighton Museum and Art Gallery decided to hold an exhibition of her work, to run from 15 January to 20 February. In the catalogue, now itself a collector's item, exhibitions organiser, Betty O'Looney, wrote, "This exhibition conforms to one of the present aims of this Museum. This is to make a specialised collection of the decorative arts of the twentieth century." She went on to explain that the idea for the exhibition had come initially from Martin Battersby, whose collection formed the nucleus of the exhibition. She continued, "Clarice Cliff herself has been most helpful; she has provided us with comments, now dovetailed into the text of this catalogue. She modestly showed surprise that anybody should take an interest in her work today!"

Clarice was by now in her early seventies, but she wrote a lengthy and lucid description of the early days of Bizarre and made brief comments about some of the pottery on display, several items of which she not only lent for the exhibition but after it gave to the Museum, which today has one of the best collections of her work in the country. Though Clarice neither told her family about the exhibition nor visited it herself, understandable in view of the long journey, the fact that she co-operated so fully and generously with the Museum is proof enough that she took pleasure in the accolade it bestowed. When, in the October of that year, she died after a brief and sudden illness, aged 73, it was with the knowledge that her work was being collected, appreciated and preserved as an outstanding example of influential ceramic design, the commercial success of which had been vital in keeping her workforce in full employment during the dark days of the Depression.

An Idyll plate (£650/$960) with two items in Tulips, vase (£400/$590), preserve jar (£500/$740).

Top row: 'Mondrian' (£1200/$1775) and 'Red Picasso Flower' (£1200/$1775), with below 'Branch and Squares' (£500/$740) and a sandwich plate in Hydrangea (£200/$295), also produced in a green colourway. (Courtesy of Christie's)

Interest in Art Deco generally and in Clarice Cliff in particular continued to build up with an inexorable momentum. A leading London gallery, L'Odeon in the Fulham Road, held a exhibition of her work in 1976, accompanied by a limited edition book by Peter Wentworth-Sheilds and Kay Johnson (reprinted in 1981) with a foreword by Bevis Hillier, who likened Clarice to "an archetypal Arnold Bennett heroine", such as his Anna of the Five Towns. He compared her "cosy genius" to that of Enid Blyton, saying both had "the same mixture of genuine feyness and business acumen". The book, with its wealth of biographical detail and handsome colour plates has inevitably become yet another collector's item. By now the antiques trade had realised that though not antique as such, being far less than a hundred years old, items of Clarice Cliff pottery were collectable and had started to fetch comparatively high prices. At first confined to sophisticated London galleries and antiques markets, by 1980 a few enterprising provincial shops, notably in York, Saffron Walden and Warwick, had found out about Clarice Cliff and had become places of pilgrimage to collectors nationwide. One enthusiastic collector, Len Griffin, decided in 1982 to form the Clarice Cliff Collectors Club with the aim of researching information and building up a photographic archive. In 1983 Christie's held a small but influential auction devoted entirely to her work, and the high – for those days! – prices focussed trade attention on Clarice as a money-spinner. In fact every Art Deco artefact was now eagerly sought, and the first Art Deco fairs were being organised by Top Hat Fairs of Nottingham. Held in a nightclub in the town and later moved to Loughborough Town Hall, they were a magnet for collectors and dealers alike.

In the summer of 1985 Midwinter produced a limited edition of reproductions of Clarice Cliff

An Original Bizarre sugar bowl and jug (£300/$445), with similar items in Green House (£1000/$1480). (Courtesy of Christie's)

A twin-handled Lotus jug in 'Cubes' (£5000-£7000/$7400-$10,710). (Courtesy of Christie's)

pieces as a tribute to her growing fame, carefully identifying them by a special backstamp as modern ware. There were, naturally, problems in production, since some of the colours used by the Bizarre girls are now banned, as containing toxic substances like cadmium and lead, so substitutes had to be found. Again, in order to obtain the authentic freedom of execution and the correct weight of colour, the modern paintresses needed retraining in the style of freehand painting originally used, and luckily ten of the Bizarre paintresses were persuaded to oversee the work.

A television series, *Pottery Ladies* on Channel 4, included Clarice along with Charlotte Rhead and Susie Cooper, arousing considerable public interest. Perhaps inevitably in 1986 came the news that fake items of Clarice Cliff pottery were turning up for sale in London and elsewhere, but fortunately they were clearly bogus, with patchy Honeyglaze and poor handpainting. Swift action by the auction house, Phillips, in the form of an identikit for recognising the fakes, put an end to the scare, which had at least served a useful purpose in alerting collectors to the possibility of trouble of this kind. Meanwhile, large collections of genuine articles were being built up by enthusiasts and some of these were put on display in various parts of the country. In connection with the Warwick Arts Festival, a local collector's pieces were put on display at Warwick Museum, drawing visitors from all over Britain and even abroad. Since only a brief catalogue had been issued, this led to an illustrated pocket reference-book based on the collection called *Collecting Clarice Cliff* published the following year. Also in 1988 a large coffee-table book was issued jointly by Len Griffin and an American collector, Louis K. Meisel. Both these books in their different ways supplemented the excellent newsletters of the Clarice Cliff Collectors Club.

Two jugs from the Original Bizarre range (£400/$590 each).

Conical teaware in 'Bignou' (£700/$1035), with teapots in Citrus (Delecia) (£800/$1185) and Orange Trees and House (£1500/$2220). (Courtesy of Christie's)

24

Interest in Art Deco and in Clarice Cliff continued to grow, with newspaper and magazine articles, television items and, above all, with the well-publicised specialist auctions now held at Christie's and other major auction houses. There was even a play, *The Bright and Bold Design*, about the Clarice Cliff Cinderella story. More reproductions, this time by Wedgwood, were produced with meticulous attention to detail, and the London-based Kevin Francis Ceramics put on the market colourful Toby jugs, figurines and facemasks of Clarice Cliff, later adding a whole range of other leading ceramicists. As interest and prices escalated, a plethora of Clarice-related novelties flooded onto the market – plates, placemats, ornaments, even teatowels, knitting patterns and cardigans, rather along the lines of the ubiquitous Edwardian Lady range, suggesting a certain bandwagon element in the proceedings. Perhaps this was confirmed by an article recently in *The Guardian* Money Section one Saturday which stated, "Few areas of collecting can have matched the advances seen for Clarice Cliff pottery". A Christie's spokeswoman agreed "People queue for hours before the auction starts."

All of which is fine from a commercial point of view. But Clarice Cliff's work is valuable and worth collecting, not because it costs a lot of money now and is a good investment for the future, but because it is full of genuine joie de vivre. Wherever you see it, whether in an exclusive London gallery or a dusty church hall, it lifts the heart. It has the power to make the sun come out on the darkest winter day. And, as the song says, who could ask for anything more?

A great girl, Clarice Cliff.

Strong geometric shapes and patterns – a Conical Tennis jug (£2500/$3700) and Football bowl (£1500/$2220), a 'Sunspots' vase (£2500-$3700) and 'Zavier' rose bowl (£1000/$1480), with May Avenue (£7000/$10,360), a landscape with geometricised trees. (Courtesy of Christie's)

A banded Bonjour teapot, milk and sugar (£200/$295).

Clarice Cliff Chronology

1899 Clarice Cliff born January 20, at 19 Meir Street, Tunstall, Staffordshire. The family later moved to Edwards Street, Tunstall.

Father: Harry Thomas Cliff, an iron moulder. Mother: Ann Cliff, née Machin. Brothers: Harry, Frank. Sisters: Sarah, Hannah, Dorothy, Ethel, Nellie.

1909 Left the High Street Elementary School to go to the Summerbank Road School.

1912 Left school to learn freehand painting at Lingard, Webster & Co., Swan Pottery, Tunstall.

1915 Left the Swan Pottery to learn lithography at Hollinshead & Kirkham, Unicorn Pottery, Tunstall. Attended evening classes at Tunstall School of Art, later transferring to Burslem School of Art.

1916 Joined A.J. Wilkinson's Royal Staffordshire Pottery, Burslem.

1920 Wilkinson's took over the Newport Pottery in Newport Lane, Burslem, adjoining their site. Clarice Cliff promoted to work as a gilder, with John Butler and Fred Ridgeway, Wilkinson's leading designers, on the Tibetan, Oriflamme and Rubaiyat ranges.

1923 The Wilkinson Archives has a note 'C.C. does the gold', referring to Pattern No.7309 on a plaque by Fred Ridgeway.

Orange Roof Cottage £3000/$4440.

Honolulu £2500-£3000/$3700-$4590.

1924 Early figurines, including two men in Arab dress marked 'Clarice C 24' and an old market woman marked 'C.C.24'.

1925 Clarice Cliff moved to 40 Snow Hill, Hanley, a one-bedroom flat over a beauty salon. She was given a studio in Newport pottery with facilities to produce the firm's publicity photographs. Comment was caused by her close association with Colley Shorter, the firm's managing director, a married man 17 years her senior.

A part smoker set, Berries. £2500/$3700.

1927 Between March 14 and May 26, Clarice Cliff took a short course in sculpture at the Royal College of Art at her employers' expense, her address being given as Campbell House, 90 Sutherland Terrace, Maida Vale, W8. Later this year she visited Paris, again at her employers' expense, to study Continental design. Returning to Newport Pottery, she began decorating a large stock of old-fashioned whiteware with brightly-coloured geometric patterns. A 15-year-old apprentice, Gladys Scarlett, assisted her.

1928 More apprentices – Annie Berisford, Mary Brown, Nellie Harrison, Clara Thomas, Nancy Liversedge, Vera Rawlinson and Cissie Rhodes – joined the team, enabling a production line to be set up. Joan Shorter Baby Ware was launched, based by Clarice Cliff on drawings by Colley Shorter's eight-year-old daughter.

Bizarre, the name chosen by Clarice Cliff, began to be used in July. Soon her name was added. The first press

A rare shape vase, Gibraltar, £2800/$4145.

advertisement for **Bizarre Ware** appeared in August backed up by an in-store demonstration in London and a preview at the British Industries Fair.

In September, Ewart Oakes, Wilkinson's chief salesman, took **Bizarre Ware** to sell in Berkshire. His success led to more orders, and more apprentices, boys as well as girls, were added to the team.

A Bizarre backstamp was created, including Clarice Cliff's signature. Later this year **Crocus** began and continued in various versions until 1963. **Lupin** was also entered into the pattern-book but does not seem to have been put into production.

1929   **Fantasque** introduced as an additional range name.

Shapes: *Archaic and Conical*, Patterns included Diamonds, Garland, Lightning, **Lodore**, **Kandina**, **Broth** (until 31) **Inspiration** (31) **Latona** (31) **Latona** tree (30) **Lily** (30) **Ravel** (35) **Sunray** (30) **Trees and House** (31) **Umbrellas and Rain** (30).

By the end of the year, the whole of the Newport Pottery was given over to **Bizarre Ware**.

1930   Shapes: *Stamford* and *Eton* table-ware. **Age of Jazz** figures. Patterns included Branch & Squares, Carpet, **Flora**, **Floreat**, Orange Battle, **Orange House, Persian** (2), Sliced Fruit, Sunburst, Red Tulip, Yoo Hoo. **Applique Avignon** (until 31) **Applique Lucerne** (32) **Applique Windmill** (31) **Autumn** (33) **Berries**

Honolulu,
£2500/$3700.

Applique Red Tree,
£6000-£8000/$8880-
$12,240.

(31) **Inspiration Knight Errant** (31) **Latona Dahlia** (31) **Melon** (33) **Oranges** (31) **Original Delecia** (32) **Scraphito** (31).

1931 Shapes: *Stamford* fancies and *Daffodil.* *Conical* sugar dredger

Nuage and **Cafe Au Lait** techniques.

Patterns included: **Tennis, Marigold, Woodland, Applique Idyll** (until 35) Bobbins (33) **Farmhouse** (32) **Gardenia** (32) **Gibraltar** (32) **House & Bridge** (33) **Mountain** (32) **Etna** (32).

Solitude, £2500/$3700.

1932 Shapes: *Chick* cocoa pot and *Elephant* napkin rings

Patina and **Damask Rose** techniques

Patterns included **Forest Leaves, Hollyrose, Canterbury Bells** (until 33) **Chintz** (33) **Delecia Citrus** (33) **May Avenue** (33) **Orange Roof Cottage** (33) **Sungay** (33)

Initiation of experiment to involve artists in production of designs for tableware.

Orange House, £4000/$5920.

1933 Commissioned work from artists in production.

Shapes: *Bonjour* and *Biarritz* tableware.

Goldstone range, *Lynton* shapes, Blackbird pie funnels, facemasks **Marlene, Flora, Chahar**

Patterns included Car and Skyscraper, **Devon, Japan, Solitude, Coral Firs** (until 36) **Cowslip** (34), **Delecia Pansy** (34) **Delecia Poppy** (34) **Honolulu** (34) **Secrets** (37) **Windbells** (34)

Green House, £5000/$7400.

1934 Display of commissioned work – *Modern Art for the table*. **Fantasque** phased out.

Shape: *Trieste*

Patterns included **Bridgewater**, **Newport**, Stencilled Deer, **Hydrangea** (until 35) **Moselle** (or 35) **Rhodanthe** (until 41 and post-war) **Viscaria** (36). The **My Garden** range (1939 and post-war)

1935 Patterns included **Fragrance**, **Pine Grove**, **Aurea** (until 37) **Cherry Blossom** (36) **Trallee** (36).

1936 Patterns included **Kelverne**, **Passion Fruit**, **Forest Glen** (until 37) Honiton (37) **Raffia** (37) **Taormina** (37).

1937 Shapes: *Windsor*, Gnome Nursery Ware. Bizarre phased out.

Patterns included **Ferndale**, **Delecia Anemone** (38). **Fruit and Basket** range

1938 Shapes: **Celtic Harvest** (until 41 and Post-war), Waterlily Range, Signs of the Zodiac.

1939 September, outbreak of war.

November 2 death of Mrs Annie Shorter.

1940 December 21, Marriage of Clarice Cliff and And Arthur Colley Austin Shorter (not announced until November 1941).

1941 Newport Pottery requisitioned by the government.

1942 No more decorated pottery for the duration of the war.

Applique Blossom. £7000-£8000/$10,360-$12,240.

Novelty Teddy Bear Bookends decorated in Black Umbrellas and Sunburst, £6000/$8880 the pair.

Novelty Gollywog Bookends, £5000/$7400 the pair.

1945	Ending of hostilities. Decorated pottery resumed for export only. Restrictions gradually eased.
1952	Wartime restrictions finally lifted completely. Coronation ware produced.
1963	December – Colley Shorter died, aged 81.
1964	Factories sold to Midwinters and Clarice Cliff retired.
1972	Brighton Museum held the first British exhibition of Clarice Cliff pottery, to which she contributed catalogue notes and items from her own collection, some of which she later gave to the Museum.
	October 23, Clarice Cliff died after a brief illness, aged 73.
1976	Publication of *Clarice Cliff* by Peter Wentworth-Sheilds and Kay Johnson, L'Odeon, London (limited edition).
1981	Reprinted.
1982	The Clarice Cliff Collectors Club founded by Len Griffin.
1983	Christie's first specialist Clarice Cliff auction.
1985	Midwinter Limited Edition reproductions.
1987	Exhibition of a collection at Warwick Musuem.
1988	*Collecting Clarice Cliff* by Howard Watson, based on this. Also publication of *Clarice Cliff and the Bizarre Affair* by Len Griffin and Louis Meisel.

Tennis, £1000/$1480.

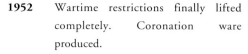
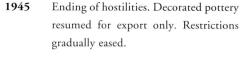

Sunray, £8000/$11,840.

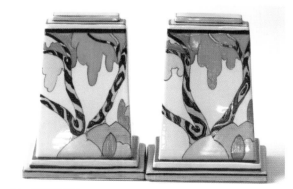

Honolulu, £5000/$7400.

1989   Specialist Clarice Cliff auctions twice yearly onwards by Christie's.

1992   Wedgwood Limited Edition reproductions.

1995   Bonham's first specialist Clarice Cliff auction.

1999   Three specialist auctions by Christie's. Clarice Cliff Centenary Exhibition at the Wedgwood Museum. Centenary events by the Clarice Cliff Collectors Club.

2000 onwards   Regional specialist auctions at Gardner Houlgate in Bath, Bonhams twice year Clarice Cliff specialist sales.

2003   New for 2003, Wooley & Wallis in Salisbury, a specialist Art Deco sale featuring major Clarice Cliff items.

From left: a rare miniature vase £750/$1110; Conical £750/$1110; Small vase £500/$740.

Range Names and Surface Techniques

Confusion is sometimes caused for new collectors by the backstamps "Bizarre" and "Fantasque", as if they are unfamiliar with Clarice Cliff's enormous range of patterns they may think that these are pattern names rather than the range names they really are. Bizarre was applied originally from 1928 to the early geometric patterns, its use later being expanded to cover also early florals and landscapes up to 1937, when it was finally discontinued. The term "Original Bizarre" was used instead for the geometric patterns from 1930. Fantasque was brought into use from 1929 to 1934, in order to offer an alternative range to Bizarre, though in fact the two ranges overlapped and the use of the two range names was primarily a marketing device, as Clarice Cliff herself admitted, when she said in her notes for the 1972 Brighton Exhibition, that "Fantasque was *supposed* to be a little different" in order to sell to a second retailer in a town where Bizarre was already being sold through an established outlet.

Banded dinnerware in the Odilon shape (£200/$295).

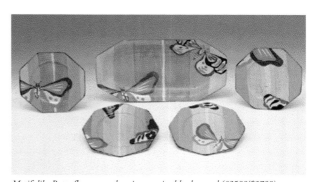

Motifs like Butterfly were used against a striped background (£2500/$3700).

Another range name was Biarritz, introduced in 1933 with its own backstamp for use on a particular rectangular shape of tableware, sometimes being seen alone, sometimes along with a Clarice Cliff mark, sometimes together with a Bizarre mark or even with all three. The Biarritz range usually had a shoulder pattern applied, often a stamp-sized version of the original pattern, though sometimes too the whole surface was covered or covered apart from the central circular area where the food would go.

In addition to these basic ranges, Bizarre, Fantasque and Biarritz, a particular surface

A vase in 'Castellated Circle' (£500/$740) with Broth (£300/$445) and Melon (£800/$1185).

technique frequently gave its name to a range of patterns, as follows:

Inspiration (1929-31) This might be said to be Clarice Cliff's "up-market" range, in that it was sold at higher prices than her other pottery. Unpopular with the paintresses – its rough surface made their fingers sore – it was marketed with considerable imaginative skill as being a long-lost secret from Ancient Egypt, and the mixture of metallic oxide glazes, black when applied, did indeed result in wonderful deep rich blues, turquoises, pale mauves and pinks. Underglaze designs included Caprice, Lily, Garden, Persian 2 and Knight Errant.

Latona (1929-31) A milky glaze combined with colourful freehand designs to give an eggshell finish that was subtle and brilliant, so that it could be advertised as "the full glory of modern colouring on beautiful satiny matt glazes of varying tones". Latona Bouquet, Latona Dahlia, Latona Red Roses and Latona Tree are some of the patterns in this range.

Appliqué (1930-33) Fairytale scenes in all-over vidid colour required great skill on the part of the paintresses as they were painted without an outline, and in the earlier examples the entire surface was covered with sumptuous colour, making it expensive to produce. Banded in eye-catching combinations of black, red and yellow, the storybook variations include, amongst others: Appliqué Avignon, Appliqué Lucerne, a castle on a hill, Appliqué Caravan and Appliqué Windmill. A later pattern, Appliqué Idyll, produced in a number of versions each showing the ubiquitous 1930s motif, the Crinoline Lady, was painted mainly in pastel shades but often with daring touches of orange and black, and sometimes with the characteristic Appliqué banding. Today the Appliqué range fetches extremely high auction prices.

Two items in the 'Bobbins' pattern, vase (£2500/$3700), beaker (£700/$1035).

'Pebbles' on a single-handled Lotus jug (£2000-£3000/$2960-$4590).

Scraphito (1930 only) Usually vases or lamp bases, this range featured deeply-moulded abstract patterns over the entire surface, the outlines picked out sometimes in pastel shades and sometimes, more effectively, in vivid colours. Never particularly popular, it appeared only briefly. Other potteries of the period had more success with their inscribed ware than Clarice Cliff with her Scraphito range, probably because the buying public expected from her more visual impact than it gave.

Delecia (1930-34) Initially produced as an experiment with glazes, the thinned colour being allowed to drip at random over the surface of the ware (Original Delecia, 1930-32), this produced brilliant and startling results. It was developed to include first, a band of fruit in orange and yellow with green leaves, topping a toning complement of runnings in grey and green, with touches of blue among the leaves (Delecia Citrus, 1932-33) and then including garlands of flowers in a similar style (Delecia Anemone, Delecia Pansy and Delecia Poppy, 1933-34). The combination of naturalistic motifs with the runnings was unusual and attractive, appealing to customers who found the bolder patterns too outré. Clarice was to use Delecia runnings much later for two popular landscapes, Forest Glen and Newlyn.

Café au Lait (1931-33) Though not a range as such, this technique added considerably to the variety of patterns on offer since it could be applied to many existing designs to give them a "new look". Applied with a sponge to give a mottled finish, it could be applied on certain areas only, leaving space for a pattern in between (eg Canterbury Bells) or all over the piece and a familiar pattern added on top (eg Oranges Café au Lait and Autumn Café au Lait). Clarice briefly returned to this technique for the sky of the landscape Trallee (1935-36). Though the name

'Carpet' Red (£7500/$11,100 plus).

The Delecia technique of allowing the paint to drip down the ware was soon adapted to include fruit and flowers. Here, Original Delecia (£200/$295), Pansy Delecia (£1500/$2220) and Citrus Delecia (£300/$445).

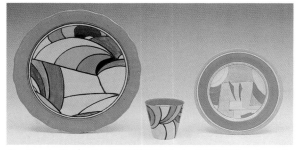

Two items in 'Swirls', plate (£1500/$2220), beaker (£400/$590) and a smaller plate in 'Xanthic' (£600/$890).

implies a coffee colour, a number of other colours were used effectively, for instance yellow, green, orange and blue.

Nuage (1931) Similar to Café au Lait, Nuage however used thickened paint so that the surface of the ware was textured like orange peel, with an area left for the application of stencilled flowers or fruit. Perhaps, like Scraphito and the later Patina, Nuage failed to become popular because the textured surface was too alien from the usual smooth-to-the-touch surface of glazed pottery.

Damask Rose (1932) This, on the other hand, was a completely smooth pinky-beige glaze, skilfully applied to present a perfect surface, with dainty floral motifs added. Time-consuming for the paintresses, it was perhaps too restrained to appeal to the buying public at the time, so it remained less popular than other ranges and was phased out.

Patina (1932) This finish took the idea of Nuage a stage further, with slip (liquid clay) in pink or grey lavishly splattered onto the surface of the ware to give it a roughened surface before glazing. Simple patterns (Patina Coastal, a seascape, Patina Country, a landscape, and Patina Tree a highly stylised tree design) were then applied. The ware was produced only briefly, as it failed to attract customers, probably because once again smoothness to the touch was expected of ceramic items.

Etching (1934-35) Like the Café au Lait technique, this was a method of paint application used across a number of patterns, rather than a range in itself. Not meant in the usual sense of the word, when an acid-etched metal plate is used to produce a repeated image, in pottery terms it describes here a method of blending brushstrokes of colour to create a shaded effect. Used for the Rhodanthe pattern in 1934, and its colour

A Sunray jug with an Orange House jug (£1000/$1480 each).

A 'Diamonds' single-handled Lotus jug (£5000/$7400) next to a 'Sunburst' vase (£2500/$3700), Orange House plate (£1500/$2220) – Autumn Jardiniere (£2000/$2960), Lotus jug (£3000/$4440), Summerhouse Isis vase (£3000/$4440) and, on the tall vase, Secrets (£1500/$2220).

Two Summerhouse items left (£750/$1110), right (£1500-£2500/$2220-$3825).

36

variations Aurea, Viscaria and Pink Pearls, it suited the taste of the later 1930s for softer colours and a more muted effect, without any hard edges. It was also used on the Trallee landscape for the thatched roof of the cottage.

My Garden (1934-39) A long-running favourite, this moulded range of bowls, vases and jugs in which brightly coloured flowers encrust the base or the handle, was according to an advertisement, "Designed by a lover of flowers for flower-lovers". It goes on to describe the pieces as "charming in their originality of design and colour, and are eminently practical". The body colours – beige, green, reddish-brown, black and matt or glazed mushroom – contrasted well with the bright floral trim and in its time the range sold well, though collectors today do not as yet regard it highly.

Goldstone (1933-35) Resulting from experiments with a different type of clay to which metallic dust had been added, this ware had a speckled surface and was given the minimum of decoration, often only outlines of geometric shapes or leaves. It is very modern in appearance, rather like studio pottery, and though at the moment not highly prized, this could change over time.

Raffia (1936) This was another range not very successful in its own day, being perhaps too ordinary in appearance, with a ribbed surface intended to imitate the craft material of the same name, and having only restrained decoration, though sometimes given an overall coloured glaze as well. Lacking the prettiness of My Garden or the stunning impact of the early patterns, Raffia, though produced in some quantity, is rarely popular with modern collectors.

Celtic Harvest (1938 and post-war) The Harvest range, with its knobbly handles of colourful fruit and flowers and its wheat sheaves moulded against a basketweave background, makes up in

Pastel Autumn items with an Orange Autumn jug (£250-£750/$370-$1150).

Conical teaware in Honolulu from £200-£3000/$295-$4590 per item. (Courtesy of Christie's)

exuberance what it lacks in subtlety. Sometimes given chrome rims or lids, it has a peasant charm all its own and though initially not popular with modern collectors it has recently become sought after and prices are rising, especially for rarer items like the fruit basket, the double jampot and the gravy-boat with its matching saucer. Certainly a display of the complete range can be very decorative and effective, especially in a cottage interior.

Waterlily (1938) Perhaps designed to appeal to those for whom Celtic Harvest was too outrageous, the Waterlily range is charming either in the cream or pale blue versions, and includes dishes, bowls, teaware and jugs, all with floral decoration to tone, the largest item, the fruit bowl, designed to look like a pink or yellow waterlily floating on a lake. The range sold well and still has considerable appeal today, usually found in good condition and at reasonable prices.

Fruit and Basket (1937) Very rarely carrying the Clarice Cliff backstamp, this range has a moulded basketweave effect on the body with moulded fruit in purple, pink and green, with an alternative colourway in orange. Only recently identified by name, it is, like Celtic Harvest, effective as a group, and so far jugs, beakers, a biscuit barrel, a cheese dish, a cress dish and an attractive large fruit bowl have been found. Other items may well turn up in the course of time, and since owing to the lack of a backstamp it is frequently unrecognised as Clarice Cliff's work, it remains very reasonable in price.

Plates in (top) Woodland (£500/$740), below Limberlost (£500/$740) and Lorna (£600/$890). (Courtesy of Christie's)

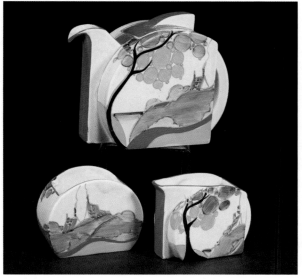

Stamford teaware in Secrets (£2000/$2960). (Courtesy of Christie's)

Backstamps and other methods of dating

Before very long the Clarice Cliff collector will acquire an instinctive eye for her designs and patterns. A collector can pick out a Clarice Cliff design on sight from among the rest of the goods on sale in a shop or on a stall at an antiques fair, a church fête or jumble sale. Picking up a bargain has been known to happen in the past but as the years go by and Clarice Cliff's name becomes more widely known, this is becoming increasingly difficult. Without even looking at the base of a discovery, the collector can feel fairly sure it is by Clarice Cliff and also can probably say from the shape and pattern whether it is an early piece, an item from the prolific middle period of her work or a later piece. With detailed knowledge of the sequence of shape introduction, one can make an informed guess as to the date of the piece to within a few years. If the pattern is a familiar one, the collector may well know the dates when it was available (setting aside the rather slim possibility that his purchase was a 'matching', that is, a piece of a pattern decorated especially for a customer who had the misfortune to break part of a set in a discontinued pattern. In the thirties, single items were made to oblige a previous purchaser, quite often several years after the pattern originally bought had been phased out).

For business reasons it was important to be ruthless in cutting out unprofitable lines and some patterns which did not catch the public's fancy survived for only a few months before being weeded out. This, of course, makes them rare today and much sought after by collectors — a kind of posthumous rehabilitation! Apart from long-running favourites like Crocus and

Some examples of Clarice Cliff backstamps

Rhodanthe, even successful patterns were only produced for a few years, for they inevitably began to lose popularity and were replaced by something more appealing to current taste.

Shape and pattern, then, will help to date an item but a more accurate guide, as with any pottery, is the backstamp – the trademark or wording stamped, printed or impressed on the base.

Many Clarice Cliff items, particularly flat pieces like plates or chargers, do have a date impressed underneath but the collector must be wary, since an impressed date may be misleading, as it is a guide only to the date of manufacture of the pottery and not to the date when the items were decorated. The impressed mark usually gives the month number above the last two digits of the year, along with, in some cases, an embossed shape number, especially on vases.

For the date of decoration an important guide is any additional information given by the wording which was put on at the same time as the pattern itself. This is possible because the form of wording altered from time to time giving us important clues about the date of production. One problematic area here is that the dates of some different marks overlapped, some of them running concurrently for a considerable while. This was because the various ranges had their own marks, sometimes used on very similar stock sold to different retailers. In particular, this applied to Bizarre and Fantasque. The Bizarre backstamp was used from 1928 until 1937 and the Fantasque from 1929 until 1934, to be followed by various Clarice Cliff only backstamps until 1963 when all stamps using her name were discontinued on the sale of the factories to Midwinters.

Initially, the information on the base was handwritten, as no stamps existed and the

Orange Bridgewater on two matching vases (£4000/$5920 pair) and Green Bridgewater on a strong geometric shape (£3000/$4440). (Courtesy of Christie's)

Coral Firs plate (£600/$890), with a vase in Capri, (£200/$295), cigarette and matchholder (£500/$740) and toast rack (£400/$590).

40

management were unlikely to have any made until the need for them was proven by a successful sales drive. As a result, 'Bizarre by Clarice Cliff' was at first handwritten, in addition to the underglaze printed factory name, and these were obviously the earliest pieces to reach the shops. The enthusiasm with which they were received clearly justified a rubber stamp to speed up marking and eventually lithographed marks which obviated the possibility of smudging and which could be applied even faster. In fact it is necessary to look very closely to distinguish between the two methods. The lithographs, naturally, were the neater of the two, the rubber stamp generally being used with black ink, though in the early days gilt and pale green inks were also used.

Handpainting continued to be used for adding the pattern name, in script at first and later in block letters, above the main stamp. When it became clear that the pattern, for instance Crocus or Gayday, was likely to continue for some time, lithographs were made for these names as well, and similarly the Inspiration range started off with INSPIRATION handwritten above it. After 1931 handwritten marks of any kind seldom appear, except on the tiny advertising plaques, the backs of which were so small a very fine paintbrush was used, for example, 'FERNDALE by Clarice Cliff', the name of the pattern being in block letters and the rest in script. On these it was essential to identify the pattern unmistakably, as they were used by the shopkeepers to inform the factory of their customers' latest orders. Collectors often wish it had been the custom to put the pattern names on every piece, but despite the advertising boast, 'Look for the name Clarice Cliff on every piece', many items undeniably from the Newport Pottery were sent out without any backstamp at all!

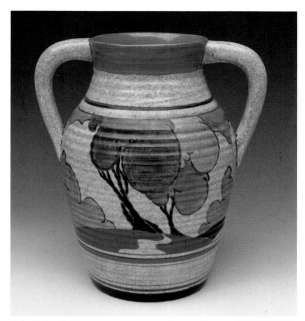

A double-handled Lotus jug in Autumn, with green café-au-lait (£2000/$2960).

Forest Glen (foreground) (£2500/$3700) with Green Erin (£3500/ $5180). (Courtesy of Christie's)

As the Newport order books began to bulge with ever-increasing sales, it became sensible to spread tax liability across the whole operation, and in 1930 'Handpainted by Clarice Cliff, Wilkinson's Pottery, England' joined the 'Handpainted by Clarice Cliff, Newport Pottery, England' used in two stamped sizes from the autumn of 1928. The range name Bizarre was used throughout and Fantasque for a short while in script, then in block letters above Bizarre. Once lithography was introduced, Fantasque appeared alone again and Bizarre as a lithograph credited, 'Newport' until 1934.

The Biarritz range, introduced by 1933, had its own distinguishing mark. This sometimes had a Clarice Cliff mark added to it as well, and sometimes a Bizarre mark too. It seems there were hardly any strict rules about backstamps. Sometimes even the base of a tea cup will carry a wealth of contradictory information whilst a large item like a meat dish carries no identifying marks at all!

From this it can be seen that even with all three strands of information — shape, pattern and backstamp — it is difficult to date any item with absolute certainty, though a fairly accurate idea can be obtained in this way. The best method of all is to date the piece by provenance — if it is being purchased from the original owner, an exact date is sometimes given:

'It was bought for us for our wedding in 1932 . . .'

'I saved up out of my first few months' wages for it in 1934 . . .'

'My Mother bought it for me to put in my bottom drawer in 1935 when I was eighteen . . .'

'I got into trouble for breaking the other two plates in 1937 when my mother had only just had that set for her fortieth birthday.'

Napkin rings in Pastel Melon, Windbells and Secrets, and Blue Firs (£250-£350/$370-$535 each).

Newlyn (£750/$1110), the blue version of Forest Glen, with beakers in Pine Grove (£250/$370), Battle (café-au-lait) (£350/$520) and Windbells (£600/$890). (Courtesy of Christie's)

This is the hard evidence that authenticates the age of a new acquisition, gives it considerable human interest and links today's collector with the time when the china shops had shelves full of the very latest Clarice Cliff designs.

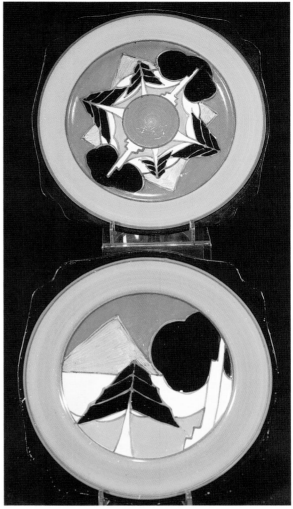

Two sandwich plates both with the pattern 'Black Luxor', but given completely different treatment in each case (£1200-£1500/$1775-$2295 each). (Courtesy of Christie's)

Collecting Clarice Cliff

One of the most intriguing aspects of collecting Clarice Cliff is the knowledge that it was originally regarded as cheap, cheerful pottery for practical use in the home. Bought in vast quantities in the Thirties, few realised how popular the quirky colours and bold designs would become – not only as 'happy' household items, but artistic treasures admired by thousands of collectors worldwide.

At the same time, it was at variance with the conventional tableware of the day, and putting it on the market at all was a gamble. Sheer chance, backed up by a clever advertising strategy, meant that what began as an experiment quickly turned into a phenomenon. The name *Bizarre* says it all.

With the benefit of hindsight, it is easy to trace all kinds of influences which may have played a part in providing inspiration for particular shapes and patterns. Like all commercial designers, Clarice Cliff studied current trends and fashions, altering them to suit her purpose and taking into account the limitations of her material and the skills of her workforce. Her designs increased in complexity as production gathered momentum – from geometric to abstract, from abstract to floral, from floral to landscape – always with colour lavishly used to brighten up the drab interiors of her day.

The sensational success of Bizarre Ware, particularly in a period of economic hardship, is proof enough that Clarice Cliff shrewdly assessed the climate of the times and was fulfilling a need for colourful and original pottery which stood out from the tableware on offer from other

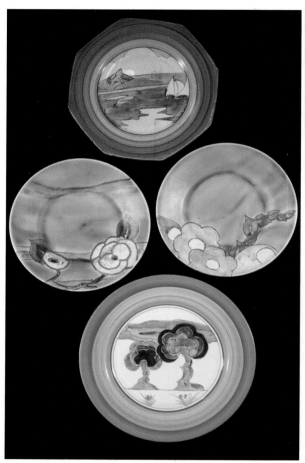

A Gibraltar plate (£1000/$1480) (top) with an Oasis plate (£600/$890), and two Inspiration Rose plates (£500/$740 each). (Courtesy of Christie's)

Patina Coastal was decorated by including liquid slip on the surface of the ware (£1000/$1480).

44

manufacturers in the industry. Not afraid to take risks, she offered bored housewives something new, and in so doing created patterns and shapes which were to hold their appeal for all time.

Patina Country (£700/ $1035).

For collectors today, particularly the design conscious, her work has many attractions. Unlike buyers in the Thirties, we now have the whole range at once to choose from, an endless variety of individual items, all instantly recognisable and each with its own special characteristics. Limited only by considerations of space and price-range, we can select the pieces we prefer from more than two thousand patterns and five hundred shapes, and seldom these days does the functional purpose enter into a purchase. When did you last put lupins in your **Lotus** jug, or teabags into your **Stamford** teapot?

An added pleasure is the search. Not for us the routine shopping trip into the Thirties High Street to a china shop with shelves crammed with brand new Clarice Cliff pottery. Instead we have the excitement of the early morning arrival at the antique fair, the long hours spent at the auction house, the leisurely browsing while on holiday, any of which may yield an unforeseen treasure, or equally, prove fruitless. No jumble-sale can be passed by, no junk shop, however unpromising, can be left unexplored, for, as every collector is aware, you never know . . .

We all have our own great 'finds', that elusive piece with only the faintest hairline tucked away on the top shelf of the local charity shop, or the incredible discovery at the school fête, with only a few slight chips. Collectors are the eternal optimists, like avid gardeners who believe in the pictures on the front of the seed packets. And who can blame them? For after all, whatever the weather may be elsewhere, in the world of Clarice Cliff, the sun is always shining.

A large Inspiration Knight Errant (£3000-£4000/$4440-$6120) vase with an Inspiration Caprice (£2500/$3700) vase and a House and Bridge (£2500/$3700) vase. The Inspiration range was the most expensive Clarice Cliff produced, being time-consuming and requiring careful handfinishing. (Courtesy of Christie's)

45

Notes for Collectors

Starting a Clarice Cliff Collection

Many Clarice Cliff collections have been started more or less by accident, one or two pieces being inherited and then added to in order to form a small display, which has then grown by gifts and purchases to the point at which it has become an absorbing interest. Other collectors have begun by looking for pottery to display on, say, a dresser or a set of shelves, and having got together a suitable selection have found that buying Clarice Cliff pieces has been so enjoyable they don't want to give it up. It might also be said to be addictive, and when pieces are discovered in good condition and at the right price, they are very hard to resist. Perhaps the pattern with the most perennial appeal is **Autumn (or Original) Crocus**. Originally the most popular in Clarice Cliff's own day, it still remains the one most frequently chosen by first time purchasers. Only later do they gain confidence to add to their collection the more outrageous colour combinations of **Sunray**, **Gardenia** or **Umbrellas & Rain**. **Spring Crocus** is a gentle feminine pattern which is easy to live with; **Melon** is a striking addition to a sophisticated interior and **Celtic Harvest** is the exact opposite, looking its best in a cottage style interior. So wide is the range of Clarice Cliff's work that there is something which will appeal to everybody. The only problem lies in deciding what and how to collect. Most people begin by collecting indiscriminately and only later decide to set parameters for themselves, selling off early purchases which no longer fit in with now established tastes and preferences.

On the right, Inspiration Aster (£1000/$1480), with on the right, Inspiration Bouquet (£1000/$1480), and two more Inspiration vases (£800/$1185 each). (Courtesy of Christie's)

An Inspiration Persian Yo-yo vase (£5000-£7000/$7400-$10,710). (Courtesy of Christie's)

A display limited to one favourite pattern can be very impressive, since all resources have been devoted to a single objective: to get together as many different pieces as possible of the chosen pattern. The opposite extreme is to aim to cover as many patterns as possible. Since Clarice Cliff is estimated to have designed around 2000 patterns altogether it is unlikely that anyone will manage to find them all! This is an approach which is attractive, as it allows a quick start to a collection, limited only by the financial budget of the purchaser.

A third way might well be to emulate the original purchasers of Clarice Cliff pottery by buying items selected to fit in with your existing decor. This is a sensible approach, since whichever method you choose you will always be limited by the available space, and by this system you will be buying particular pieces for particular places in your home.

Another approach is to select a shape which fits you pocket and your surroundings. Where plenty of money and plenty of wall space are available, a display of plates is perhaps the most decorative way of showing off a range of patterns, combined with plaques and chargers.

It is worth noting that chargers are dish shaped and the plaques plate shaped, though they were made in the same sizes and both were usually wall hung. Chargers, though, could be used as fruit dishes or even paired together in a wooden frame to make a two-tier 'occasional' table. A display of plaques and chargers alone would be stunning but may also be prohibitively expensive. If space is limited, as well as finance, a collection of smaller items would be effective; coffee cans perhaps or 'trios' (cup, saucer and tea plate) for instance.

One shape which displays particularly well is

Inspiration Bouquet (£1500-£2000/$2220-$3060). (Courtesy of Christie's)

Latona Fantasy Flowers (£1000-£2000/$1480-$3060) in foreground, with Diamonds (£3500/$5180). (Courtesy of Christie's)

the *Conical* sugar shaker, since this allows patterns to be seen very effectively and a variation might be to include *Conical* salt and pepper shakers too, contrasting the large with the small. A miniature collection would be ideal for a single cabinet including perhaps ash trays, coasters, cauldrons, toast racks and the smaller candlesticks. The ultimate, of course, would be a collection of *Lotus* jugs and *Isis* vases, but few collectors are likely to contemplate such an outlay.

Record Keeping

If your collection has been begun by an inheritance or by pieces given to you by elderly relatives, you may find as your collection grows that you want to exchange some of your original items for more suitable additions. Damaged items, too, bought perhaps for the sake of acquiring a rare pattern or unusual shape, will probably be replaced once perfect specimens become available. You may be in a position to buy frequently, or your budget may limit you to the occasional purchase. Gifts may come your way at certain times of the year and if these are out of line with your existing pieces it is useful to know a friendly dealer who will take them in part exchange for something else, or possibly sell them for you on a sale or return basis. But however you get your collection together and whatever your guiding principle, it is essential to keep a written record of your transactions, perhaps with photographs as well, giving each purchase a number and writing down its cost, the date purchased, who sold it to you and a brief description of its shape, pattern and condition. This is vitally important because if and when you decide to sell it, you will need to think back perhaps several years – not something easily done from memory. Though the main pleasure of collecting is the beauty of the pieces individually and together, the bonus that it will

Inspiration Newport (£1000/ $1480). (Courtesy of Christie's)

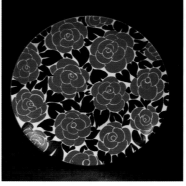

Latona Tree (£1000/$1480), with the rare Black colourway of Broth (£3500/$5180). (Courtesy of Christie's)

Perhaps Latona Red Roses was the most effective of all (£1500–£2000/$2220–$3060). (Courtesy of Christie's)

probably be a good investment cannot be overlooked, and even if you never sell a single piece of it your record is proof that you have spent your money wisely as prices rise – and there is every indication that they will continue to do so.

Insurance

This talk of monetary values raises the question of insurance. A modest collection can usually be included in your general household insurance but it is essential to raise the matter with your insurers in case there is a top limit and you have acquired one or more very expensive items – a *Lotus* jug for example. Also, one must be aware of parts and sets because if you have a tea or coffee set and you break one cup, that one cup may be all you will be covered for, even though a set worth several hundred pounds has been ruined. Larger collections will require a separate insurance and should be updated each year to take into account new purchases and rising prices, and equally any selling off which may have taken place.

The premium is naturally proportionate to the total value of the collection but the peace of mind will be worth it. One way to bring it down a little is to install a burglar alarm and special locks on at least the windows and doors of the room where the collection is kept. However, average collectors should be careful not to let these precautions spoil their pleasure in having the collection. It seems very unlikely that anyone would deliberately set out to steal fragile objects like pottery, when more portable items like jewellery and silver provide less hazardous targets, so the main danger your collection is in will be accidental damage rather than theft. If an item does get broken, or even just cracked or chipped, you will need to decide how to approach the insurance company. Polaroid photographs of the broken pieces are invaluable, especially if accompanied by a signed letter from a reputable

From top: Sunray (£500/$740), Latona Grape (£500/$740) with Zap (£600/$890). (Courtesy of Christie's)

Latona Dahlia (£2000-£3000/$2960-$4590) and Latona Inca (£700-£1000/$1035-$1530). The Latona range used a milky glaze to enhance the vivid colours of the patterns. (Courtesy of Christie's)

dealer to the effect that such and such an item, current market value £x, has been seen "damaged beyond repair" or "damaged but restorable at a cost of £x". It is important to note that restoration will reduce the value of the item by quite a proportion. Depending on its extent, this reduction should be stated and claimed for in your application.

Restoration

Restoration is, in fact, a question fraught with "ifs and buts". There is all the difference in the world between knowingly buying a restored piece and buying one by accident, only finding the restoration afterwards. If restoration is pointed out by the seller, and you decide to buy the piece nevertheless (perhaps because it is a rare pattern which you are unlikely to find elsewhere), this is quite acceptable and the price will take the restoration into account. One caution though: be careful to note in your collection record not only that the piece is restored but where the restoration has been carried out. New techniques and modern materials are constantly coming into use, making restoration very difficult to detect, so trust is essential between buyer and seller. If you buy a piece on which you later find restoration, the item should be taken back to the seller – who should refund your money – "Caveat emptor", or "let the buyer beware" is not a motto by which a dealer can trade if he values his reputation and wants to build up a circle of regular and satisfied customers. It is always wise to examine any item very thoroughly in a good light. Spouts and handles should be checked with particular care and a finger run round rims and bases, as touch is often a better guide than sight. Look out, too, for any slight variation in colour. The chemical composition of the colours used in Clarice Cliff's day are in some cases now no longer permitted for reasons of health and safety and modern colours

Latona Dahlia (£2000/$2960) (top) with Trallee (£2000/$2960) and Idyll (£3000/$4440). (Courtesy of Christie's)

A rare Grotesque landscape face mask, Honolulu. £10,000-£15,000/$14,800-$22,950.

50

are usually fairly easy to detect when in close proximity to the original handpainting.

Lighting and Display

As your collection grows you will eventually find that the original space allotted to it becomes too small. What then? One appropriate solution, if you can find room for it, is an Art Deco china cabinet, a simple, angular one if you prefer, or perhaps an eye-catching circular one if the rest of your decor can accommodate it. After all, a large proportion of Clarice Cliff's output was probably displayed in just such cabinets throughout the Thirties, though you will perhaps want to add a modern touch by introducing some unobtrusive lighting to show off your pieces, the glass shelves letting the light shine through from top to bottom. If you feel something more up-to-date will fit your room better, adjustable glass shelves housed in an alcove can be fitted, with sliding glass doors to keep out dust, again with suitable lighting. Aluminium and glass cases of the kind found in jewellery or antiques shops are also widely available but these may seem to you too much like turning your home into a museum, though they are excellent for office displays or foyers. As a background to your collection, however you display it, framed posters from the various Clarice Cliff exhibitions are ideal, or perhaps reproductions of original Bizarre advertisements.

Rarity

Despite the Depression, and thanks to designers like Clarice Cliff, the Thirties were years of high output in the pottery industry and competition was keen among the leading manufacturers like Wilkinsons, Fieldings, Shelley and Myott. Had all the pottery that was produced survived, there would have been ample for all of today's collectors, but in fact much of the output was tableware, used constantly and frequently broken.

A saucer (£200/$295) by Eva Crofts and a Biarritz plate (£100/$150) by Gordon Forsyth.

A plate by Duncan Grant (£30/$45).

A Laura Knight bowl (£200-£300/$295-$460).

Decorative objects like vases and flower jugs were in less danger, but they too occasionally came to grief in the course of accidental encounters with household pets or an over zealous cleaner. The Second World War led to the putting away of superfluous items of decoration "for the duration" and boxes of pottery and ornaments were stored more or less safely in the loft along with pictures whose glass, shattered in an air raid, might cause injury. Sometimes the boxes were brought down again after the war, sometimes not. Changing tastes condemned their contents as 'old fashioned' and much Thirties pottery was thrown out or given to jumble sales where it was sold for a few pence. What had been a flood of brightly coloured, handpainted pottery before the war was reduced to a trickle. In consequence, the rediscovery of Clarice Cliff and the rising demand for her work throughout the Seventies and Eighties found only a comparatively small amount available in the market place. If this was true of the once ubiquitous **Original Crocus**, it was even more true of patterns originally produced for only a limited period. In other words, all Clarice Cliff is rare, but some patterns are rarer than others and some shapes are very rare indeed.

Without doubt the rarest range of all is **Appliqué** and this experimental range is highly prized by collectors. Other experimental techniques such as **Latona** and **Inspiration**, although desirable, they are less high prized or priced. Variations on the **Crocus** theme, the **Blue Crocus** and the rarer **Purple Crocus** are very sought after, while **Honolulu**, **Sunray** and **House & Bridge** are three patterns which always fetch high prices. **Tennis** is another rare pattern and **Butterfly** too is seldom seen for sale. Of the later patterns, **Forest Glen**, Clarice's last landscape is one of the most popular of all. Items

A 'Circus' plate (£1000/$1480) by Laura Knight and two 'Chevaux' plates (£100/$150 each) by John Armstrong, with plates in Berries (£800/$1185), Citrus (Delecia) (£200/$295), 'Floreat' (£300/$445) and Acorn (£150/$220). Between 1932 and 1934 distinguished artists were commissioned to produce designs for pottery. (Courtesy of Christie's)

A single dancing couple, one of the set of five Age of Jazz figurines, £10,000–£15,000/ $14,800–$22,950.

52

from the pottery designed by famous artists of the day are novelties which enhance any collection, especially those of Dame Laura Knight's Circus range. These are always worth watching out for as they add interest by providing a variation to the main collection which was designed by Clarice herself. It is easy to see which shapes are likely to be the rare ones, as any unusual fins or flanges meant a risk of warping in the kiln, while pieces obviously made in several sections joined together were expensive to produce and were only made in small quantities, to be further reduced by their fragility and consequent breakages.

As time passes, various factors operate to affect the collecting fields. Books, articles, television programmes and much publicised auctions act as catalysts. On the one hand they arouse interest and make more people keen to buy Clarice Cliff pieces and on the other they bring out of hiding fresh examples of her work from people who did not previously realise they were sitting on a gold mine. Also, more people are now dealing in Art Deco in general, many of them with a bias towards the Pottery Ladies and this means there is a wider spread of specialist shops and stalls in antique markets, as well as Art Deco fairs in London and elsewhere. However the proven investment value of Clarice Cliff means that as important pieces disappear into private collections, they are unlikely to reappear on the open market again. Thus, although from time to time prices may stabilise there is only a limited amount to satisfy demand and any stimulus from the media can send prices rocketing up again.

Availability and Sources
Supposing, then you have decided to start buying Clarice Cliff or to add to the pieces you already own? You will have to be prepared to put in much time and effort as well as money if you are to achieve more than merely average success. Apart

The rarest of the Age of Jazz figurines, the much prized 'Double Dancer', £20,000-£30,000/$29,600-$45,900.

Reverse side of the 'Double Dancer'.

Single Dancing couple. Note the different position of the hands to that on the opposite page. £10,000-£15,000/$14,800-$22,950.

from the specialist auctions of Clarice Cliff pottery, held mainly in London, and the occasional pieces in general auctions across the country, probably the best way to add to your collection is to get to know the specialist Art Deco dealers in your own area and then range further afield, making your wants known. A phone call first is advisable as closing days vary from town to town and there is nothing worse than travelling a long distance only to find the shop you plan to visit is closed. An advantage with this plan is that established dealers have their reputations to consider and are likely to be keen to build up a client list with a view to future sales, so transactions with them will be smooth and satisfactory. Buying at a shop or in an antiques centre is a more leisurely affair than at auction, and you can probably obtain reassuring information as to provenance in many cases, which adds to the interest of the piece and sometimes helps in dating. Prices, too, are usually fixed with an eye to future sales to regular customers, though overheads and therefore profit margins inevitably vary in different parts of the country. At auction there's always the chance of a bargain but equally the danger of paying too much in the heat of the moment, as well as the buyer's premium to consider. Probably both carefully considered purchases over a shop counter and successful bids at auction must go into the building up of a serious collection.

Then, of course, there are the fairs. Nowadays most fairs include dealers selling Art Deco pottery and on their stalls there are sometimes pieces by Clarice Cliff, as well as some that crop up on the more general stalls. People often have the impression that public admission times mean that most of the important dealing is done within the trade before the public are allowed to enter, but provided you get to a fair early it is possible to

The Pianist and Guitar Player from the Age of Jazz figurines, £10,000-£15,000/$14,800-$22,950.

The Drummer and Saxophonist from the Age of Jazz figurines, £10,000-£15,000/$14,800-$22,950.

Applique Blossom. £5000-£7000/ $7400-$10,710.

find choice pieces which have only just been unwrapped and put out to fill up spaces. Many fairs now have early admission at a higher price, which you may find it worthwhile to pay as it puts you on a footing with visiting trade buyers. Some fairs, too, are now so huge that the earlier you start your visit the better, especially as often there are hundreds of outside pitches as well as those under cover in the main pavilions. Of more specific interest are the specialist Art Deco fairs where there is likely to be some Clarice Cliff pottery on nearly every stall, unless the dealer is selling, say mainly lighting or furniture. The increasingly popularity of the 1920s and 1930s, has also spread more thinly the available stock for dealers and collectors alike, especially as many of the choicest pieces are reserved for the big London auctions. For this reason alone it is important to foster good relations with the dealers you know and trust, so that your collection will benefit from the best they have on offer.

Football. £8000-£12,000/$11,840-$18,360.

While there is little point in asking a dealer to "ring me when you have any Clarice Cliff in", a specific request will often bring results, as a dealer will watch out on his travels for items he knows he can sell as soon as he gets home again by means of a single phone call. Similarly, let other collectors know what lines you are following, so that if they are offered pieces they don't want themselves they will bear you in mind. If they have pieces you covet, drop a hint or two, so that if they decide to sell they will give you a 'first refusal'. Keep an eye on auctioneers' advertisements as they will usually mention any Clarice Cliff items they have on offer in the small print and while the big auction houses attract dealers from all over the country, smaller firms in your own area may go unnoticed except by the local trade, which may not include anyone

Autumn in Red. £5000-£7000/$7400-$10,710.

bidding on 'modern' pottery. Getting to know a porter who will bid for you saves hours of tedious sitting in auction rooms and is well worth the occasional tip to keep him happy. And, of course, the Internet is a whole new ballgame!

Most dealers, thanks to the Pottery Ladies series and headline auctions, are au fait with Clarice Cliff prices and may indeed be highly over-optimistic regarding their prices for quite ordinary pieces that come their way, but there is always the chance that a small gem may turn up in your local junk shop or perhaps at a school bazaar where the organisers have failed to have their bric-a-brac checked by a local dealer. If you do make a discovery, it is as well to be generous, especially if the function is for charity. Paying a little more than you are asked, provided the item is worth it, will ensure that on another occasion you are offered any similar items, perhaps being given 'first pick'. So be sure to leave your phone number. If a **Crocus** jampot was sent to the jumble sale this time, next time the sender may decide to get rid of their **Sunray Lotus** jug – who knows?

Red Summerhouse £5000-£7000/$7400-$10,710.

Information about fairs, shops and auctions can be found in a number of ways. Those in your own area will usually be advertised in your local press, while magazines for collectors carry advertisements for those further afield. For a really comprehensive coverage it is possible to subscribe to the trade press, that is, the *Antiques Trade Gazette* and the *Antiques Bulletin*, both weekly and available on subscription, but also sold at many major fairs. Useful, too, is the smaller monthly publication *The Collector*, and the annual *Guide to the Antique Shops of Great Britain* is handy to keep in the car. Fairs guides are proliferating, too, as for more and more people collecting antiques of all kinds is becoming an absorbing hobby, and these can be bought at

Football, £5000-£7000/ $7400-$10,710.

fairs, while most organisers put out free leaflets with information about the dates and venues of their future events.

Armed with information from some or all of these sources, it will be possible to plan your time to the best advantage, and your collection will benefit from you being in the right place at the right time, that combination of hard work and good luck which lies behind the building up of every successful collection.

Fakes

Early in 1986, Clarice Cliff collectors were alarmed to read in the press that fake *Lotus* vases had begun to turn up in London and before long, elsewhere. Investigation proved, however, that the fakes were so poorly produced that they could be spotted fairly easily and all the major London auction houses refused to handle suspect vases offered to them once the initial alert had gone out. Though considerable trouble had been taken to reproduce exactly the Bizarre backstamp, patchy, uneven toffee-coloured Honeyglaze was a giveaway, while the unglazed bottom rim was narrow compared with the genuine vase. Not only this but the standard of painting was so poor that neither Clarice Cliff nor the art director of any reputable pottery would have accepted it. The inefficiency of the producers of the bogus vases was irritating, to say the least. After all, they were peddling large pieces and hoping for high prices – anyone likely to be paying such large sums of money would have sufficient knowledge to suspect anything so obviously substandard.

Phillips, the auctioneers, with commendable speed, issued an identikit, consisting of three coloured photographs, showing a genuine **Summerhouse** *Lotus* vase and a fake geometric vase. These pictures are top, bottom and sideways

Orange Roof Cottage £5000-£6000/$7400-$9180.

House and Bridge. £5000-£6000/$7400-$9180.

on, accompanied by a list of points to watch out for when offered a doubtful piece.

For dealers and collectors the scare was short lived but for the general public the effect lasted longer and occasionally, even today, those fakes are nervously mentioned by people who have seen only the sensational headlines and not read the real facts of the matter.

Unfortunately, it seems possible that the question of fakes will once again be in the news, as recently badly-faked *Conical* sugar shakers and at least two Lotus jugs have surfaced in the Midlands, but have been swiftly detected owing to the poor quality of the painting and also the low price – £80 for something which, if genuine, would cost three times as much. Trading Standards officers have been alerted and once again the problem is being speedily resolved, so perhaps this time shock-horror headlines will be avoided.

Far more serious is the rumour that arises from time to time that a different form of faking is in operation – that of adding Clarice Cliff patterns, usually the more sought after ones like **House & Bridge** to plain items already genuinely backstamped "Clarice Cliff". Advice is sometimes given, "When in doubt, coin it!" That is, scratch the suspect paintwork with the edge of a coin or something similar. Few collectors, however, are likely to have the nerve to risk damaging a valuable item – to say nothing of enraging an honest dealer! – by dragging a coin across the paintwork of a plate or jug. Everyone knows that the surface of perfectly genuine pieces may have been scratched in the course of normal wear, even though the on-glaze handpainting was given a final firing to protect it, and also that some colours, especially dark blue, were fugitive and faded with use.

Again, modern detergents can sometimes have a

Red Autumn £5000-£7000/$7400-$10,710.

One of the 12 Zodiac Star Signs: Aquarius. £1000/$1480.

disastrous effect, as for instance, when the oranges on Crown Ducal **Orange Tree** turn brown with the use of washing up liquid containing bleach. A collector's best protection is to buy from a reputable dealer with, if possible, some indication of the item's provenance. However, the safest rule, guaranteed to avoid altercations, acrimony and regrets is, "When in doubt, don't buy it".

Applique Idyll £2500-£3500/$3700-$5355.

Price and Pattern Guide

Diamonds, £10,000–£12,000/$22,200–$18,360.

In preparing or using a price guide for Clarice Cliff pottery, it must be borne in mind that prices are bound to vary in accordance with collecting trends, with the economic climate, with regional disparities, and above all with different overheads and profit margins. However, what might be called the "desirability factor" remains surprisingly constant, so that if one item is worth today twice as much as another item, the proportion of the prices is likely to remain constant. Pattern, shape and condition are the three factors which must be taken into consideration, with perfect pieces being assumed in this guide.

Red Summerhouse, £8000–£10,000/$11,840–$15,300.

That said, the only real guide as to the value or worth of a particular piece is the amount that the collector is prepared to spend. The existence of gaps in a collection will, of course, be a spur to the collector to make further purchases, while the price he is asked to pay will depend to a large extent on the rarity of the piece or pieces he has in mind – and how fashionable the pattern is at the moment! In any transaction it is important that the price paid should be one satisfactory to buyer and seller alike, otherwise their on-going relationship will be jeopardised, either by the former feeling cheated or the latter disgruntled by excessive haggling.

Though all the above needs to be taken into account, experience indicates that general guidelines exist for a core of Clarice Cliff items, assuming them to be in good condition, free from restoration and bearing appropriate backstamps. As pattern is paramount, the following guide divides items according to pattern.

Solitude, £8000–£10,000/$11,840–$15,300.

Remember too, that rarity doesn't always equate to desirability. So don't be too keen to pay premium prices for 'rarity'.

Price range 1 covers patterns made in considerable quantity and therefore fairly readily available, including **Crocus**, **Ravel**, **Rhodanthe** and similar.

Price range 2 covers patterns harder to find, being made over a shorter time-span either because of their complexity or through lack of popularity at the time.

Price range 3 covers rare patterns, including experimental ware, and must be regarded as particularly flexible since it is especially subject to current trends. It includes all the patterns made in ranges like **Appliqué**, plus special geometric patterns like **Blue W**, **Sliced Circle** and **Lightning**, rare landscapes like **Honolulu** and **Solitude**, and items from Dame Laura Knight and Eva Crofts. Impossible to evaluate except on an individual basis, prices given here are based in the main on known sales.

Note: Not all items, of course, were made in every pattern, and it is not suggested that they were. But surprises are always possible!

Price category 1

Acacia; Acorn; Alton Towers; Amber Rose; Anenome; Arizona; Aura; Aurea; Autumn Green cafe au lait; Avon; Bamboo; Banded; Batanga; Battle cafe au lait; Beechwood; Bermuda; Bignou, Blue Eyed Marigold; Blue Heaven; Blueberry Tree; Braidwood; Brunella; 'Bunch' Crocus; Buttercup; Cabbage Flower; Canterbury Bells; Capri; Celtic Harvest; Cherry; Cherry Blossom; Cherry Tree; Chestnut; Christine; Citrus Delicia; Clematis; Costal Oak; Crab Apple; Crayon Scenes; Crazy Paving; Crepè de Chine; Cruiseware; Damask Rose; Dijon Dolphins; Dorè; Dryday;

Honolulu £6000-£8000/$8880-$12,240.

House and Bridge. Plate £1500/$2220, Trio £4000-£5000/$5920-$7650.

Blue Chintz £300/$445, Nasturtium variant £300/$445.

61

Duncan Grant; Eating Apples; Exotic; Feather & Leaves; Floreat; Florida; Flower Music; Flower Wave; Foam; Forest Leaves; Fuchsia; Full Circle; Galleon; 'Garland'; Gayday; Gloria; Goldstone; Gordon Forsyth; Hawthorn; Hello; Hollyhocks; Honeydew; Honiton; Hydrangea; Indian Summer; John Armstrong; Kandina; Kelverne; Latona Tree; Leaf Tree; Lily; Lodore; Lupin; Lydiat; Marquerite; May Blossom; 'Milano'; Moonflower; Morning; Mowcop; My Garden; Napoli; Nasturtium; Nemesia; Newport; Nuage; Oranges cafe au lait; Original Bizarre; Original Crocus; Original Delicia; Passion Fruit; Patina Coastal; Patina Country; Patina Tree; Petunia; Pinegrove; Raffia; Rainbow; Ravel; Rhodanthe; Sandon; Scraphito; Sliced Fruit; Soloman's Seal; Spire; Spring Crocus; Stile & Tree; Stroud; Summer Dawn; Sungay; Sungleam Crocus; Sungold; Sunshine; Tahiti; Taomina; Tartan; Tibetan; Trent; Viscaria; Waterlily; Wheat; Winsome; Yahoo; Yuan. *Items ranging between price category 1 and 2: Branch & Squares; Brookfields;* Broth; Chalet; Clovelley; Delicia Peaches; Elizabethan Cottage; Fragrance; Ferndale; Green Chintz; Killarney; Mango; Oasis; Moselle; Shark's Teeth; 'Umbrellas'; Wax Flower; Woodland Fragrance.

Café £7000-£10,600/$10,360-$16,220.

Bowls

Bowl, complex shape, Daffodil, Conical, stepped etc,

Large Size	£300-£1000/$445-$1530
Medium Size	£300-£700/$445-$1070
Small Size	£275-£500/$405-$765

Bowl, simple shape

Large Size	£225-£400/$335-$610
Medium Size	£200-£250/$295-$385
Small Size	£150-£200/$220-$305

Jardinières, Lotus Jugs, Isis Vases

Fern pot	£175-£300/$260-$460

Orange Trees and House £5000/$7400.

Isis Vase
Large	£200-£1000/$295-$1530
Small	£200-£600/$295-$920

Jardinière
Large	£200-£800/$295-$1225
Small	£100-£500/$150-$765

Lotus Jug,
doubled-handled	£200-£1500/$295-$2295
Single-handled	£200-£1500/$295-$2295

Jugs
Athens,
Large	£100-£600/$150-$920
Medium	£100-£400/$150-$610

Bonjour, Conical,
Large	£100-£500/$150-$765
Medium	£100-£400/$150-$610
Small	£50-£300/$75-$460

Windsor, Perth, tankard £50-£500/$75-$765

Football, £10,000-£12,000/$14,800-$18,360.

Miscellaneous
Candlestick, tall, ziggurat	£100-£500/$150-$765
Candlesticks, pair, squat, cube, conical	£100-£700/$150-$1070

Cruet (or muffineer)
    (salt, pepper, mustard pot/cover)
Conical, Bonjour	£200-£500/$295-$765
Cruet, waisted items	£150-£225/$220-$345

Fruit set   (1 large bowl, 6 small)
£150-£900/$220-$1375
Individual fruit bowl	£20-£120/$30-$185

Individual grapefruit dish,
flange ends	£95-£250/$140-$385

Pair salt/pepper,
Bonjour, Conical	£100-£400/$150-$610
Pair salt/pepper, waisted	£100-£300/$150-$460
Toastrack, large	£100-£500/$150-$765
Toastrack, small	£100-£350/$150-$535

Autumn, £5000-£8000/$7400-$12,240.

Patterned Novelties

Ashtray, coaster	£50-£200/$75-$305
Beakers	£50-£250/$75-$385
Biscuit barrel/cover	
shapes 335, 336, cylindrical, EPNS mounted	
	£150-£450/$220-$690
Bookend, single, Teddy Bear, Golliwog,	
patterned base	£500-£1000/$740-$1530
Cauldron, large	£100-£500/$150-$765
Cauldron, small	£100-£400/$150-$610
Cheese dish/cover	£300-£350/$445-$535
Cigarette box/cover	£200-£500/$295-$765
Cigarette holder,	
match holder	£100-£500/$150-$765
Duck eggcup, 6 eggcups	£200-£1000/$295-$1530
Eggcup set on plate,	
4 eggcups	£100-£500/$150-$765
Inkwell, complete	
with covers	£100-£800/$150-$1225
Muffin dish/cover	£250-£275/$370-$420
Sabot (or clog), large	£100-£500/$150-$765
Sabot, small	£100-£500/$150-$765
Sardine box,	
butter box/cover	£100-£600/$150-$920
Single eggcup, footed	£50-£150/$75-$230
Single eggcup, squat	£50-£100/$75-$155
Smoker's set (complete)	
(tray, 4 ashtrays, cigarette box/	
cover, matchholder)	£200-£1000/$295-$1530

Preserve Pots (with cover)

Apple honeypot, large	£100-£300/$150-$460
Apple honeypot, small	£50-£200/$75-$305
Beehive honeypot, large	£100-£700/$150-$1070
Beehive honeypot, small	£100-£500/$150-$765
Bonjour preserve pot	£100-£500/$150-$765
Cherry honeypot	£50-£250/$75-$385
Cylindrical preserve pot	£50-£450/$75-$690
Daffodil preserve pot	£50-£500/$75-$765

Sugar Shakers

Bonjour	£200-£750/$295-$1150

Latona Dahlia. £5000-£7000/$7400-$10,710.

Lodore, cup £250/$370, teapot £750/$1110.

Left: Honolulu £5000-£6000/$7400-$9180; Solitude, £6000-£7000/$8880-$10,710.

Conical	£200-£750/$295-$1150
EPNS topped shaker	£150-£400/$220-$610

Teaware

Biarritz plate 22.5cm wide	£50-£600/$75-$920
Coffee Pot shapes (a)	£100-£500/$150-$765
Coffee Pot shapes (b)	£100-£750/$150-$1150
Coffee Set shapes	
(a) for 6	£200-£1500/$295-$2295
Coffee Set shapes	
(b) for 6	£200-£2000/$295-$3060
Coffee cup/saucer,	
solid handle	£85-£350/$125-$535
Coffee cup/saucer,	
open handle	£85-£350/$125-$535
Early Morning Set (or Tea for Two) – Teapot,	
milk jug, sugar basin, 2 cups/saucers, biscuit	
plate, shapes (b)	£500-£2000/$740-$3060
Plate 17.5cm	£50-£300/$75-$460
Plate 23cm	£50-£400/$75-$610
Sandwich set	
(tray + 6 plates)	£300-£800/$445-$1225
Sandwich tray,	
29.5cm long	£75-£250/$220-$385
Sugar Basin (round)	£50-£200/$75-$305
Sugar Basin Bonjour,	
Conical, large	£150-£400/$220-$610
Sugar Basin Bonjour,	
Conical, small	£100-£350/$150-$535
Teacup/saucer, open handle	£50-£295/$75-$450
Teacup/saucer, solid handle	£50-£400/$75-$610
Teapot (a) Windsor, Globe, Lynton, Daffodil,	
Athens	£100-£500/$150-$765
Teapot (a) with matching milk jug,	
sugar basin (sometimes also called a "Trio")	
	£150-£700/$220-$1070
Teapot (b) Bonjour, Conical,	
Stamford	£400-£1000/$590-$1530
Teapot (b) with matching	
milk jug, sugar basin	£500-£1500/$740-$2295

Orange House, £5000-£7000/$7400-$10,710.

Circus by Laura Knight, plate £1500-£2000/$2220-$3060, candlesticks £2000-£4000/$2960-$6120.

Teaset 21 piece
    Shapes (a)   £300-£1500/$445-$2295
    Shapes (b)   £400-£1800/$590-$2755
Teaset 23 piece (inc Teapot)
    Shapes (a)   £400-£2000/$590-$3060
Trio (cup, saucer, plate)
    open handle   £50-£400/$75-$610
Trio, solid handle   £75-£500/$220-$765

Vases

Flower baskets   £200-£1000/$295-$1530
Miniature vases   £200-£600/$295-$920
Vase, complex shape with fins, flanges etc.,
    Large   £250-£1500/$370-$2295
    Small   £250-£1000/$370-$1530
Vase, simple shape
    Large   £250-£1000/$370-$1530
    Small   £250-£800/$370-$1225

Wall plates and Chargers

Plaques, chargers
    30cm diam   £200-£1000/$295-$1530
    35cm diam   £300-£1500/$445-$2295
    40cm diam   £500-£2500/$740-$3825
Wall plate 23cm (decorated surface)
                          £200-£300/$295-$460

Price category 2

Apples; Arabesque Archaic; Artists In Industry;
Autumn; Beachball; Blue Chintz; Blue Crocus;
Blue Daisy; Blue Ribbon; Bowling; Circles &
Squares; Clouvre; Cornwall; Cowslip; Delecia
Anemone; Delecia Daisy; Delicia Pansy; Delicia
Poppy; Devon; Farmhouse; Forest Glen;
Gardenia; 'Geometric Flowers'; Green Bridge-
water; Green Erin; Japan; Keyhole; Line Jazz;
Lisbon; London; Lorna; 'New Flag'; Newlyn;
Orange Autumn; Orange Autumn; Orange
Bridgewater; Orange Chintz; Orange Secrets;
Orange Trees and House; Pansy Delecia; Pastel
Autumn; Pastel Melon; 'Pebbles'; Peter Pan
Crocus; Pink Tree; Poplar; Red Tulip; Secrets;

Marine £100/$150.

Mountain, £3000/$4440.

66

'Sunburst'; 'Sunray Leaves'; Trallee; Tulips; Windbells; 'Xanthic'; 'Zavier'; *Items ranging between price category 2 and 3:* Comets; 'Cubes'; Inspiration Caprice; Inspiration Knight Errant; Inspiration Persian; 'Lightning'; 'Mondrian'; Orange Battle; Persian; 'Red Picasso Flower'.

Bowls

Bowl, complex shape, Daffodil, Conical, stepped

Large	£700-£1500/$1035-$2295
Medium	£500-£1250/$740-$1915
Small	£450-£1000/$665-$1530

Bowl, simple shape

Large	£400-£800/$590-$1225
Medium	£300-£600/$445-$920
Small	£200-£400/$295-$610

Jardinières, Lotus Jugs, Isis Vases

Fern pot	£750-£2500/$1110-$3825

Isis Vase

Large	£700-£2000/$1035-$3060
Small	£600-£1500/$890-$2295
Jardinière, large	£600-£1500/$890-$2295
Jardinière, small	£400-£1200/$590-$1835

Lotus Jug

Doubled-handled	£750-£2500/$1110-$3825
Single-handled	£750-£2500/$1110-$3825

Jugs

Athens

Large	£600-£1000/$890-$1530
Medium	£500-£800/$740-$1225

Bonjour, Conical

Large	£600-£1200/$890-$1835
Medium	£500-£800/$740-$1225
Small	£400-£700/$590-$1070

Windsor, Perth tankard

Large	£300-£600/$445-$920
Medium	£250-£500/$370-$765

Honolulu Bonjour vase. £1500-£2000/$2220-$3060.

Original Bizarre 'Fancy', £2500-£3500/$3700-$5355.

Miscellaneous

Candlestick, tall, ziggurat £400-£1000/$590-$1530

Candlesticks, pair, squat,

    cube, conical   £500-£1200/$740-$1835

Cruet (or muffineer)

    (salt, pepper, mustard pot/cover)

    Conical, Bonjour   £500-£1200/$740-$1835

Cruet, waisted items   £500-£800/$740-$1225

Fruit set (1 large bowl, 6 small)

        £750-£1500/$1110-$2295

Individual fruit bowl   £100-£250/$150-$385

Individual grapefruit dish,

    flange ends   £250-£350/$370-$535

Pair salt/pepper,

    Bonjour, Conical   £200-£600/$295-$920

Pair salt/pepper, waisted   £200-£500/$295-$765

Toastrack, large   £300-£600/$445-$920

Toastrack, small   £250-£450/$370-$690

Patterned Novelties

Ashtray, coaster   £150-£350/$220-$535

Beakers   £200-£900/$295-$1375

Biscuit barrel/cover

    shapes 335, 336, cylindrical,

    EPNS mounted   £500-£1500/$740-$2295

Bookend, single, Teddy Bear, Golliwog,

    Patterned base   £1000-£2500/$1480-$3825

Cauldron, large   £400-£650/$590-$995

Cauldron, small   £400-£650/$590-$995

Cheese dish/cover £400-£700/$590-$1070-$1070

Cigarette box/cover   £400-£1000/$590-$1530

Cigarette holder,

    match holder   £300-£600/$445-$920

Duck eggcup, 6 eggcups   £750-£1500/$1110-$2295

Eggcup set on plate,

    4 eggcups   £400-£550/$590-$840

Inkwell, complete with

    covers   £500-£1250/$740-$1915

Muffin dish/cover   £300-£600/$445-$920

Sabot (or clog), large   £350-£950/$520-$1455

Applique Lugano, £500-£600/$740-$920.

Blue Firs £5000/$7400.

Secrets £2000-£3000/$2960-$4590.

Sabot, small	£350-£850/$520-$1300
Sardine box, butter box/cover	£400-£1000/$590-$1530
Single eggcup, footed	£150-£300/$220-$460
Single eggcup, squat	£100-£250/$150-$385
Smoker's set (complete) (tray, 4 ashtrays, cigarette box/cover, matchholder)	£1000-£3500/$1480-$5355

Café: a rare Eton shape coffee pot and complete coffee service.

Preserve Pots (with cover)

Apple honeypot, large	£300-£600/$445-$920
Apple honeypot, small	£300-£500/$445-$765
Beehive honeypot, large	£500-£1000/$740-$1530
Beehive honeypot, small	£500-£850/$740-$1300
Bonjour preserve pot	£450-£850/$665-$1300
Cherry honeypot	£200-£450/$295-$690
Cylindrical preserve pot	£300-£850/$445-$1300
Daffodil preserve pot	£450-£1000/$665-$1530

Sugar Shakers

Bonjour	£500-£1250/$740-$1915
Conical	£700-£1800/$1035-$2755
EPNS topped shaker	£350-£750/$520-$1150

Teaware

Biarritz plate 22.5cm wide	£500-£1200/$740-$1835
Coffee Pot shapes (a)	£500-£1000/$740-$1530
Coffee Pot shapes (b)	£500-£1500/$740-$2295
Coffee Set shapes (a) for 6	£1500-£4000/$2220-$6120
Coffee Set shapes (b) for 6	£2000-£4500/$2960-$6885
Coffee cup/saucer, solid handle	£400-£650/$590-$995
open handle	£400-£650/$590-$995
Early Morning Set (or Tea for Two) – Teapot, milk jug, sugar basin, 2 cups/saucers, biscuit plate, shapes (b)	£1500-£3500/$2220-$5355
Plate 17.5cm	£250-£450/$370-$690
Plate 23cm	£300-£600/$445-$920

Flanking the Summerhouse charger (£7000-£10,000/$10,360-$15,300), Farmhouse (£800/$1185) and House and Bridge (£1200/$1775) plates, with Solitude (£1200/$1775) and Windbells (£700/$1035) plates below and vases in Orange Autumn (£1500/$2220), Secrets (£1000/$1480) and Summerhouse (£3500/$5180).

69

Sandwich set
   (tray + 6 plates)   £750-£2500/$1110-$3825
Sandwich tray,
   29.5cm long   £250-£850/$370-$1300
Sugar Basin (round)   £150-£250/$220-$385
Sugar Basin Bonjour, Conical,
   Large   £250-£450/$370-$690
   Small   £200-£400/$295-$610
Teacup/saucer,
   open handle   £150-£450/$220-$690
   solid handle   £300-£750/$445-$1150
Teapot (a) Windsor, Globe, Lynton,
   Daffodil, Athens   £500-£850/$740-$1300
Teapot (a) with matching milk jug, sugar basin
   (sometimes also called a "Trio")
         £750-£1250/$1110-$1915
Teapot (b) Bonjour, Conical,
   Stamford   £800-£1750/$1185-$2680
Teapot (b) with matching milk jug,
   sugar basin   £1000-£2500/$1480-$3825
Teaset 21 piece
   Shapes (a)   £1000-£3500/$1480-$5355
   Shapes (b)   £1500-£4000/$2220-$6120
Teaset 23 piece (inc Teapot)
   Shapes (a)   £1750-£4500/$2590-$6885
Trio (cup, saucer, plate)
   open handle   £500-£900/$740-$1375
   solid handle   £500-£1200/$740-$1835

Vases

Flower baskets   £50-£1500/$75-$2295
Miniature vases   £400-£1000/$590-$1530
Vase, complex shape with fins, flanges etc.
   Large   £750-£2000/$1110-$3060
   Small   £500-£1500/$740-$2295
Vase, simple shape,
   Large   £500-£1800/$740-$2755
   Small   £400-£1500/$590-$2295

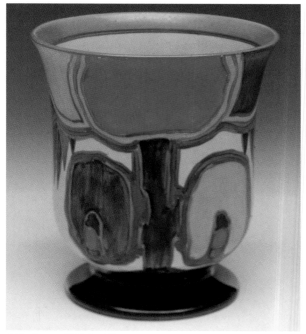

A Kandina vase (£700/$1035).

Landscapes including Summerhouse, Trees and House, 'Leaf Tree', Autumn, House and Bridge, with a Lotus jug in Melon (£500-£7000/$740-$1070).

Wall plates and Chargers

Plaques, chargers

30cm diam	£750-£1800/$1110-$2755
35cm diam	£1000-£2500/$1480-$3825
40cm diam	£1500-£3500/$2220-$5355

Wall plate, 23cm

(decorated surface)	£300-£850/$445-$1300

Price category 3

Appliqué Avignon; Appliqué Bird of Paradise; Appliqué Blossom; Appliqué Caravan; Appliqué Eden; Appliqué Etna; Appliqué Garden; Appliqué Lucerne; Appliqué Lugano; Appliqué Monsoon; Appliqué Red Tree; Appliqué Windmill; Black Luxor; Blue Firs; Blue Luxor; 'Blue W'; Cafe; Car & Skyscraper; Carpet Red; Clouvre Bluebell; Eva Crofts; Cubist; Diamonds; Football; Gibraltar; Green Firs; Green House; Honolulu; House & Bridge; Kew; Latona Dahlia; Laura Knight; Marigold; Monsoon; May Avenue; Mountain; Orange House; Orange Roof Cottage; Pink Roof Cottage; Propellor; Purple Crocus; Sliced Circle; Solitude; Sunray; Sunspots; Tennis. *NB: No upper limit is priced on items in this special top category as auction prices seem to hit major 'highs' for these desirable designs.*

Bowls

Bowl, complex shape, Daffodil, Conical, stepped

Large	£1500+/$2220+
Medium	£1000+/$1480+
Small	£750+/$1110+

Bowl, simple shape

Large	£1000+/$1480+
Medium	£800+/$1185+
Small	£600+/$890+

Jardinières, Lotus Jugs, Isis Vases

Fern pot	£1000+/$1480+
Isis Vase, large	£3000+/$4440+
Isis Vase, small	£1500+/$2220+
Jardinière, small	£1000+/$1480+

Red Roofs (£1500-£2000/ $2220-$3060).

May Avenue £15,000-£20,000/$22,200-$30,600). (Courtesy of Phillips)

Jardinière, large	£2000+/$2960+
Lotus Jug	
Doubled-handled	£3000+/$4440+
Single-handled	£3000+/$4440+

Jugs

Athens, large	£1200+/$1775+
Athens, medium	£1000+/$1480+
Bonjour, Conical	
Large	£1200+/$1775+
Medium	£1000+/$1480+
Small	£900+/$1330+
Windsor, Perth, tankard	
Large	£500+/$740+
medium	£400+/$590+

Rudyard, the pastel colourway of Honolulu, a Stamford shape biscuit barrel without the lid (£700/$1035).

Miscellaneous

Candlestick, tall, ziggurat	£800+/$1185+
Candlesticks, pair, squat, cube,	
conical	£1000+/$1480+
Cruet (or muffineer)	
(salt, pepper, mustard pot/cover)	
Conical, Bonjour	£1000+/$1480+
Cruet, waisted items	£750+/$1110+
Fruit set (1 large bowl, 6 small)	
	£1000+/$1480+
Individual fruit bowl	£200+/$295+
Individual grapefruit dish,	
flange ends	£350+/$520+
Pair salt/pepper,	
Bonjour, Conical	£600+/$890+
Pair salt/pepper, waisted	£500+/$740+
Toastrack, large	£500+/$740+
Toastrack, small	£400+/$590+

Patterned Novelties

Ashtray, coaster	£300+/$445+
Beakers	£750+/$1110+
Biscuit barrel/cover	
shapes 335, 336, cylindrical,	
EPNS mounted	£1000+/$1480+
Bookend, single, Teddy Bear, Golliwog,	
patterned base	£2000+/$2960+

Appliqué Windmill. £2000-£3000/$2960-$4590.

Cauldron, large	£750+/$1110+
Cauldron, small	£750+/$1110+
Cheese dish/cover	£750+/$1110+
Cigarette box/cover	£1000+/$1480+
Cigarette holder,	
match holder	£1000+/$1480+
Duck eggcup, 6 eggcups	£1500+/$2220+
Eggcup set on plate,	
4 eggcups	£1000+/$1480+
Inkwell, complete with	
covers	£1000+/$1480+
Muffin dish/cover	£750+/$1110+
Sabot (or clog), large	£750+/$1110+
Sabot, small	£750+/$1110+
Sardine box, butter	
box/cover	£1000+/$1480+
Single eggcup, footed	£250+/$370+
Single eggcup, squat	£200+/$295+
Smoker's set (complete)	
(tray, 4 ashtrays, cigarette box/cover,	
matchholder)	£2500+/$3700+

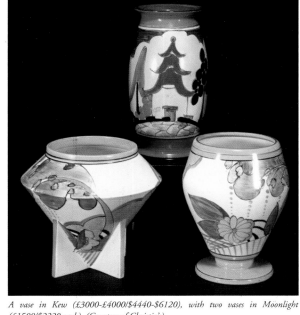

A vase in Kew (£3000-£4000/$4440-$6120), with two vases in Moonlight (£1500/$2220 each). (Courtesy of Christie's)

Preserve Pots (with cover)

Apple honeypot, large	£750+/$1110+
Apple honeypot, small	£700+/$1035+
Beehive honeypot, large	£1000+/$1480+
Beehive honeypot, small	£1000+/$1480+
Bonjour preserve pot	£1000+/$1480+
Cherry honeypot	£700+/$1035+
Cylindrical preserve pot	£700+/$1035+
Daffodil preserve pot	£1000+/$1480+

Sugar Shakers

Bonjour	£1500+/$2220+
Conical	£2500+/$3700+
EPNS topped shaker	£1000+/$1480+

Teaware

Biarritz plate	
22.5cm wide	£1200+/$1775+
Coffee Pot shapes (a)	£1000+/$1480+
Coffee Pot shapes (b)	£1500+/$2220+

Three sandwich trays, two with Red Trees and House and the other with 'Blue Luxor'. From top, £500/$740, £1000/$1480, £500/$740. (Courtesy of Christie's)

Coffee Set shapes (a)	
for 6	£5000+/$7400
Coffee Set shapes (b)	
for 6	£6000+/$8800+
Coffee cup/saucer,	
solid handle	£750+/$1110+
open handle	£750+/$1110+
Early Morning Set (or Tea for Two) Teapot, milk	
jug, sugar basin, 2 cups/saucers, biscuit plate,	
shapes (b)	£3500+/$5180+
Plate 17.5cm	£500+/$740+
Plate 23cm	£1000+/$1480+
Sandwich set	
(tray + 6 plates)	£3500+/$5180+
Sandwich tray,	
29.5cm long	£1000+/$1480+
Sugar Basin (round)	£300+/$445+
Sugar Basin Bonjour, Conical	
Large	£500+/$740+
Small	£400+/$590+
Teacup/saucer,	
Open handle	£500+/$740+
Solid handle	£750+/$1110+
Teapot (a) Windsor, Globe, Lynton,	
Daffodil, Athens	£1000+/$1480+
Teapot (a) with matching milk jug,	
sugar basin (sometimes also	
called a "Trio")	£1500+/$2220+
Teapot (b) Bonjour, Conical,	
Stamford	£2000+/$2960+
Teapot (b) with matching milk jug,	
sugar basin	£3000+/$4440+
Teaset 21 piece	
Shapes (a)	£5000+/$7400+
Shapes (b)	£6000+/$8880+
Teaset 23 piece (inc Teapot)	
Shapes (a)	£7500+/$11,100+
Trio (cup, saucer, plate)	
open handle	£1250+/$1850+
Solid handle	£1500+/$2220+

Always inspired by nature, one of Clarice Cliff's first floral patterns was her bestseller, Crocus, shown here with a vase in the Lupin pattern. The teaware includes teapots in Original Crocus (£850/$1260), Purple Crocus (£2000/$2960) and Blue Crocus (£1250/$1850), a teaplate in Spring Crocus (£45/$65) and a trio in 'Bunch' Crocus (£200/$295), with a salt and pepper set in Sungleam (£250/$370). A selection of Peter Pan Crocus £500/$740 plus.

A sponging technique called "Café-au-lait" was often used for variety. Canterbury Bells (£600/$890) combined it with handpainted flowers. Solomon's Seal (£850/$1260) used a transfer outline touched in with handpainting.

The Celtic Harvest range, moulded with fruit and corn, has become increasingly popular over the years. Footed Bowl (£75/$110), large Jug (£250/$370), smaller Jug (£175/$260), Lidded Bowl (£100/$150).

Vases

Flower baskets	£1500+/$2220+
Miniature vases	£1500+/$2220+
Vase, complex shape with fins, flanges etc.,	
Large	£3000+/$4440+
Small	£2000+/$2960+
Vase, simple shape	
Large	£2500+/$3700+
Small	£1500+/$2220+

Wall plates and Chargers

Plaques, chargers	
30cm diam	£2000+/$2960+
35cm diam	£2000+/$2960+
40cm diam	£3500+/$5180+
Wall plate, 23cm	
(decorated surface)	£1000+/$1480+

Novelties (approximate prices only)

Kneeling figure candleholder	
(pair)	£500+/$740+
Bookends – cottages (pair)	£500+/$740+
Bookends – birds, showgirl &	
student, etc	£1000+/$1480+
Toothbrush holders – Teddy Bear,	
Golliwog	£1000+/$1480+
Chick cocoapot, with tray	
and beaker	£300+/$445+
Teepee teapot	£400+/590+
Bookends (pair)	
various patterns	£1000+/$1480+
Viking longboat,	
various patterns	£500+/$740+
Flying Swan flowerholder,	
various patterns	£300+/$445
Rock flowerholder, 2 sizes,	
various patterns	£50+/$75+
Napkin rings (square)	£200+/$295+
Napkin rings, novelty shape,	
elephant etc	£200+/$295+

'Blue W', another strong geometric pattern (£5000-£7000/$7400-$10,710). (Courtesy of Christie's)

Lido Lady £5000/$7400.

75

Display plaques 8.5cm long,
   used by retailers to
   identify patterns   £2000+/$2960+
Star Signs   £750-£1250/$1110-$1915
Lido Lady ashtray   £3000-£5000/$4440-$7400
Wall masks, wall pockets £250-£2000/$370-$3060
"Age of Jazz" figures
   each   £6000-£20,000/$8880-$30,600
'Grotesque' heads £2000-£10,000/$2960-$15,300

Toby Jugs –

Small	£150/$220
Medium	£200/$295
Large	£300/$445
Character	£400-£500/$590-$765

Honolulu, £5000-£8000/$7400-$12,240.

Commissioned Work

Produced by Clarice Cliff from designs by famous artists of her day, these in general fetch slightly less than equivalent Clarice Cliff designs, the exceptions being work by Dame Laura Knight, especially her Circus range, prices being between £500/$740 and £15,000/$22,200, and Eva Crofts, the textile designer (Tea for Two £2500-£5000/$3700-$7650).

Later Ranges

Previously less popular ranges, like My Garden, Celtic Harvest, Waterlily and the 1937 design, Fruit and Basket, are now becoming increasingly popular, but are not as yet reaching prices like those above. A Celtic Harvest teapot usually fetches around £250-£350/$370-$535, the two sizes of jugs £175/$260 and £250/$370, with jampots £100/$150, My Garden being in the slightly lower range. Apart from the large Waterlily planter, £175-£250/$260-$385, most Waterlily items are £50-£100/$75-$150, as are those in the Fruit and Basket range. Increasing popularity is, of course, likely to cause rises in this area.

Honolulu, £2000/$2960.

Pattern Index and Dates

Numerals in brackets indicate probable price range as in the price guide, but must regarded as flexible, many other factors besides the pattern being likely to affect price, the popularity of a pattern varying widely over the years. For instance, Inspiration was very sought after in the 1980s, Appliqué was top seller for the 1990s, and it's anyone's guess what is going to be the star of the first decade of the new millennium.

Appliqué Lucerne, £5000/$7400.

Honolulu, £1500/$2220.

Advertising plaques in (foreground) Taomina, in Aurea (£1500-£2500/$2200-$3825 each plaque) and, with a double jam dish, Ferndale (£250/$370).

The Goldstone range often had handpainted geometric (£100/ $150) decoration, seen here in a vase with the red and black 'Milano' on a plate (£100/ $150).

The rare 'Morocco' pattern, unfortunately with a replacement lid.

Latona Dahlia, £2500-£3000/$3700-$4590 each.

A twin handled Lotus jug in Windbells (£3000-£4000/$4440-$6120). (Courtesy of Christie's)

Diamonds. £6000-£8000/$8880-$12,240.

Football £6000-£8000/$8880-$12,240.

Luxor, £5000-£7000/$7400-$10,710.

Luxor £5000-£7000/$7400-$10,710.

Red Broth, £7000-£10,000/$10,360-$15,300.

Applique Red Avignon, £10,000/$14,800.

Nasturtium £500/$740 each.

Applique Red Tree, £3000-£4000/$4440-$5920.

Taomina, £600/$890.

Pattern	Price Range	Dates	Page
Persian	2/3		
Peter Pan Crocus	2		
Petunia	1		
Pinegrove	1	1935	42
Pink			
Roof Cottage	3		
Tree	2		
Poplar	2		
Propellor	3		
Purple Crocus	3	briefly only	74
Raffia	1		
Rainbow	1		
Ravel	1	1929-35	8
'Red Picasso Flower'	2/3	1930	22
Red Roofs	2/3	1931	71
Red Trees and			
House	2/3	1929-31	20, 73
Red Tulip	2	1930	16
Rhodanthe	1	1934-41	8
		(and post-war)	
Rudyard	2/3	1933-34	72
Scraphito	1	1930-31	
Secrets	2	1933-37	36, 38, 42
			68, 69
Sharks Teeth	1/2		
Sliced Circle	3		
Sliced Fruit	1	1930	14
Solitude	3	1933	29, 60, 64, 69
Soloman's Seal	1	1930	74
Spire	1		
Spring Crocus	1	as Original Crocus	74
Stile &Tree	1		
'Stroud'	1	1933	20
Summer Dawn	1	pre-Bizarre	11
		to early 1930s	
Summerhouse			
Orange	2/3	1931-33	36
Red	3		56, 60, 69, 70
'Sunburst'	2	1930	30, 36

Honolulu, £1500-£2000/$2220-$3060.

Oranges and Lemons (£700-£1000/$1035-$1530).

84

Applique Lucerrne, £1000-£2000/$1480-$3060.

An octagonal bowl in Japan (£400/$590).

The Patina range – Patina Tree .(£500/$740)

Shape Guide

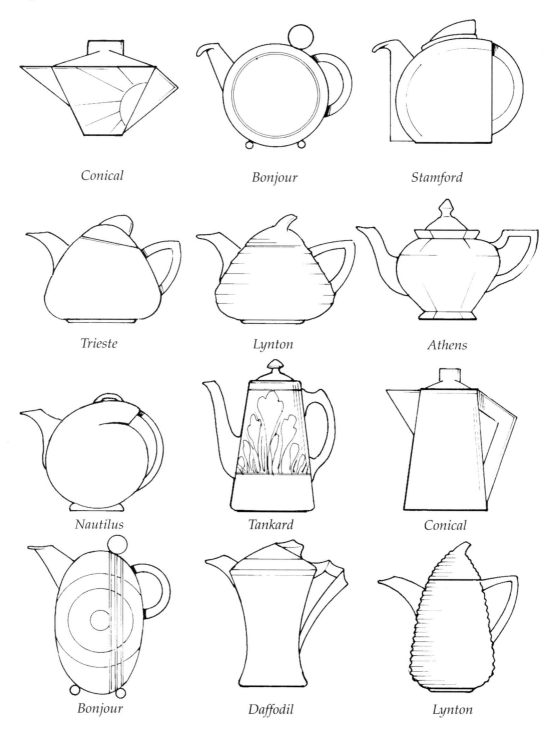

Conical

Bonjour

Stamford

Trieste

Lynton

Athens

Nautilus

Tankard

Conical

Bonjour

Daffodil

Lynton

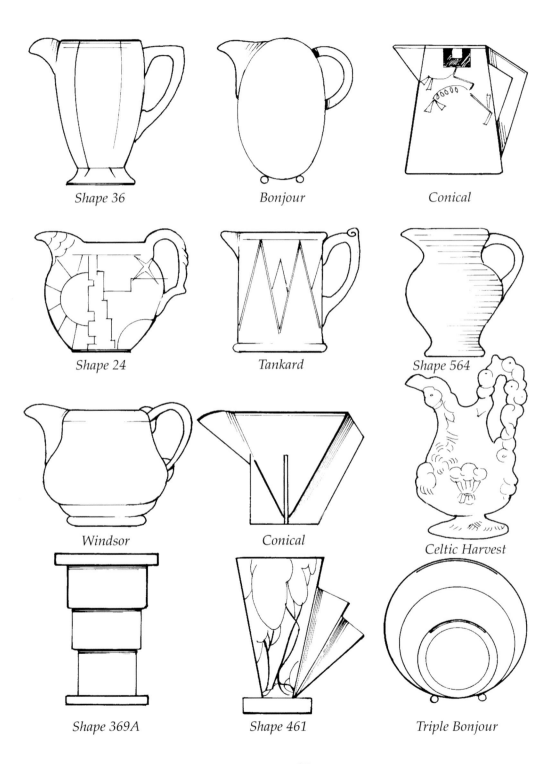

Shape 36

Bonjour

Conical

Shape 24

Tankard

Shape 564

Windsor

Conical

Celtic Harvest

Shape 369A

Shape 461

Triple Bonjour

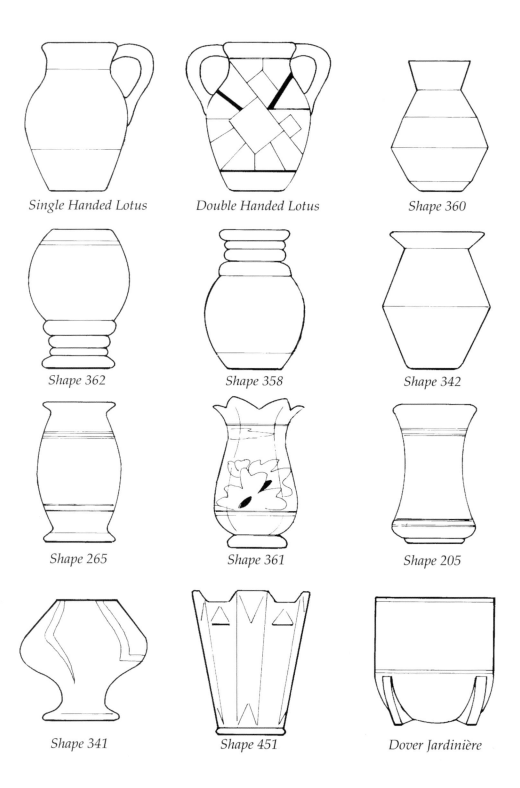

Single Handed Lotus   *Double Handed Lotus*   *Shape 360*

Shape 362   *Shape 358*   *Shape 342*

Shape 265   *Shape 361*   *Shape 205*

Shape 341   *Shape 451*   *Dover Jardinière*

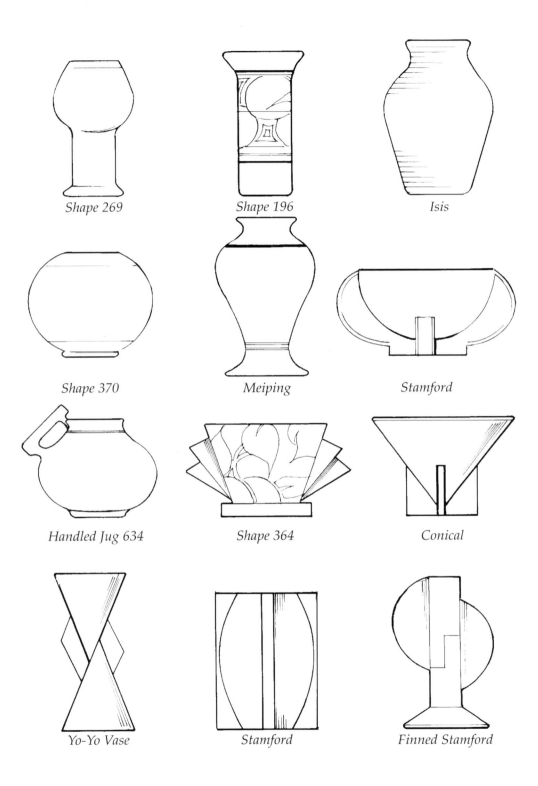

Shape 269

Shape 196

Isis

Shape 370

Meiping

Stamford

Handled Jug 634

Shape 364

Conical

Yo-Yo Vase

Stamford

Finned Stamford

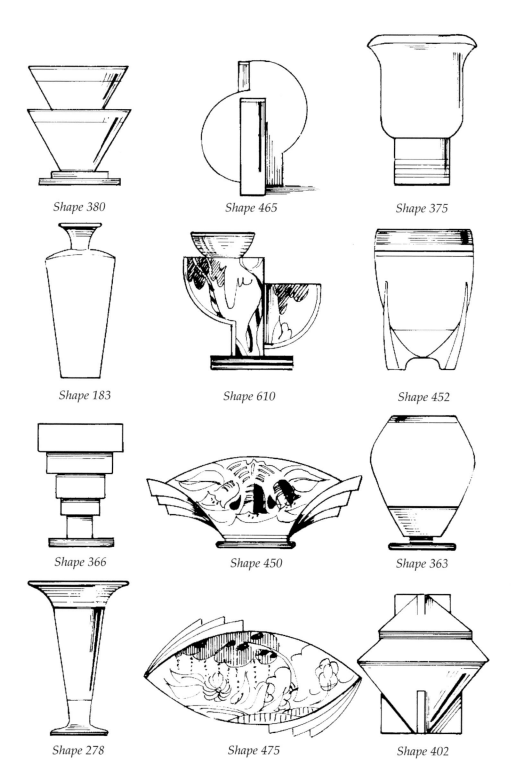

Shape 380

Shape 465

Shape 375

Shape 183

Shape 610

Shape 452

Shape 366

Shape 450

Shape 363

Shape 278

Shape 475

Shape 402

Bibliography

Clarice Cliff (exhibition catalogue), Brighton Museum and Art Gallery, 1972, occasionally available from antiquarian booksellers.

Clarice Cliff Peter Wentworth Sheilds & Kay Johnson,. L'Odeon, London 1976 & 1981.

Bizarre – Pottery by Clarice Cliff (auction sale catlaogue) second edition, priced, Christie, Manson & Woods Ltd, London, 1983.

Clarice Cliff, the Bizarre Affair Louis Meisel & Leonard R. Griffin, Thames & Hudson, 1988.

Collecting Clarice Cliff Howard Watson, Kevin Francis Publishing, 1988.

Clarice Cliff, auction sale catalogue 20/3/1989, Christie's South Kensington.

Clarice Cliff, auction sale catalogue 6/11/1989, Christie's South Kensington.

Clarice Cliff, auction sale catalogue 22/10/1990, Christie's South Kensington.

All quarterly reviews and publications by *The Clarice Cliff Collectors Club*, eidtor: Leonard R. Griffin.

British Pottery, An Illustrated Guide Geoffrey A. Godden, Barrie & Jenkins, 1974.

A Collectors History of English Pottery Griselda Lewis, Antique Collectors Club (third edition), 1985

Art Deco Tableware Judy Spours, Ward Lock, 1988

The Clarice Cliff
Collectors Club

The Clarice Cliff Collectors Club was formed by Leonard R. Griffin in 1982, and since then has researched much original material on both the pottery and Clarice's life story. With the American collector Louis Meisel, Len in 1988 produced the book *Clarice Cliff and the Bizarre Affair* which had sixy colour plates and was first published in Great Britain by Thames and Hudson. Since then he has also written a number of lavishly illustrated guides to various aspects of Clarice Cliff's work to amplify the excellent regular club newsletters.

The Club continues to research the pottery and Clarice's life and holds meetings for members each year, where new material is shown, and members have a chance to meet some of the original paintresses, Bizarre Girls, all of whom are now in their eighties.

The Clarice Cliff Collectors Club can be contacted through the Chairman:

Leonard R. Griffin
Fantasque House
Tennis Drive
The Park
Nottingham NG7 1AE